G

D1592772

Social Groups of Monkeys, Apes and Men

MICHAEL R. A. CHANCE

CLIFFORD J. JOLLY

E. P. DUTTON & CO., INC.

NEW YORK 1970

Printed in Great Britain

Contents   1556765

Illustrations

Acknowledgments

We are especially grateful to Anthony V. S. de Reuck for his persistent interest and encouragement and to Burton Benedict and Vernon Reynolds for their encouragement and comments at an early stage of preparing the manuscript. Hans Kummer kindly gave his comments on Chapter 6, and both he and Emil Menzel provided valuable unpublished material.

We should like to thank the many kind colleagues to whom we appealed for illustrations, particularly those whose names are acknowledged in the captions. We are very grateful to Dorothy Clarke for photographic assistance.

I have enjoyed the help of many friends and colleagues who have contributed both encouragement and clarification in the course of many discussions.

My wife gave invaluable assistance by typing material out of which the manuscript was constructed. Thérèse Hadley and Teresa Shiner have collated and typed the final manuscript. Special thanks go to all three for their untiring efforts and attention to detail.

MICHAEL CHANCE

NOTE ON AUTHORSHIP

C. J. J. is mainly responsible for Chapter Two, and M. R. A. C. for Chapters 3–8.

To all field workers on primates, past and future

NOTE ON TERMINOLOGY

Throughout the book we have used the term subhuman rather than nonhuman to describe primates other than man, because the flexibility and diversity of man's behavioural responses are qualitatively superior to those of other primates. Also, because man alters his environment, he is constantly readjusting to his own constructive or destructive activities. Both these capabilities are so distinctive that they seem to us to represent a level of operation in purely adaptive potential which is different from and more comprehensive than the adaptive potential of any other primate.

CHAPTER ONE

Introduction

> . . . it is clear that field investigations of the quantity
> and quality to build reliable theories of primate behaviour
> have yet to be made.'
> SHERWOOD L. WASHBURN, DAVID A. HAMBURG,
> 1965

Only within the last quarter of a century has man turned to the study of the societies of our near zoological relatives for what they may ultimately teach us about the origin and, perhaps, some of the present features of our own social habits both as individuals and societies. These new findings will no doubt have a profound influence not only on the way we think about ourselves, but also on our own behaviour.

In the first stages of acquiring this knowledge – and we are only at the beginning – we must try to see the features of these sub-human societies as they actually are. This is much more difficult than even many of today's investigators realize; not least because so much current thought about behaviour is of traditional origin and is, therefore, not necessarily appropriate to the task. This book is to an important extent a critique as well as an exposition of what has already emerged, because at this stage we cannot take as *established* all that has been reported, if only because the method of investigation may not have been adequate. To rebut, to redefine and even to offer an alternative framework of explanation is part of the fun in the early stages of a subject. The discovery of emergent patterns which form the basis of working hypotheses is as much part of the flavour of the subject as are the surprises and unique experience of the field worker.

Most field studies have been carried out by enthusiasts from disciplines other than zoology who became aware, during and after the Second World War, of the very great gap in our knowledge of the behaviour of subhuman primates. This gap had to be filled if the study of human behaviour in all its variety was to be placed within a biological context, and in the last twenty years a number of investigators, at first mainly from centres in the United States but later also from Europe and Japan, have gone out to observe the behaviour of monkeys and apes in the wild.

Very little information existed on how these observations could be made without appreciably disturbing the primates' behaviour. Often enough, with trial and error their only method, the greater part of the expeditions' time and money was expended in finding out how to obtain satisfactory and reliable information, and it was not even possible to decide which localities were desirable until a number of different methods had been tried out. Hence the paucity of information from, for example, the early expeditions of Carpenter and Washburn to study the gibbon in Siam. Yet these pioneer studies laid the foundations for present methods and inevitably still determine to some extent the scope and nature of the information obtained by modern expeditions.

The early explorers studying social behaviour who went into the societies of our close phyletic relatives for the first time were like the early field anthropologists in that they were seeking to glean as much information as possible about societies different from our own before they disappeared or were altered beyond recognition by contact with modern man. But, unlike the anthropologists, they did not approach the material with a uniform discipline of thought. Some were anthropologists, like Washburn and DeVore, others were zoologists, like Carpenter and Schaller; still others, like Hall, were psychologists, or anthropologists like Reynolds, with leanings towards zoology and an appreciation of ethology. All were restricted by inadequate funds, but impelled by the urgency of their task, and by sheer physical and mental persistence, they stretched their resources to the limit and gleaned all the information we now possess. Without doubt, however, their mode of approach and the background of their thought determined the nature of the information they brought back and also restricted the scope of their work in ways which have not been appreciated. This point is likely to be strongly debated soon, but few will deny that the differences of approach are significant.

For example, ethologists now realize that observation is the starting-point for a science of behaviour, something that was not formerly understood. But it is not easy to observe. The human mind is tuned to do two things simultaneously; to perceive and interpret. Understanding must follow, for without understanding what has been seen will not be remembered; and what is perceived can only be remembered and then expressed if it forms part of something already recognizable. Hence cultural and linguistic forms, through which observation must be expressed, will tend to predispose the field worker to a selective awareness.

The ethologist must first observe; only after prolonged observation has impressed the features of what is being looked at on his mind is he able to discern the parts, which can then be related to reveal the structure of the behaviour. That a structure exists has only just become clear.

Previous unsatisfactory attempts to generalize about causal factors underlying primate social behaviour have led workers to emphasize the diverse nature of different species, but in this book we show that there are underlying similarities about which generalizations can be made.

In the course of the book, we hope to show that primate social organization can be understood in terms of mechanisms and structures common to many mammalian societies that have been intensively investigated. For more detailed consideration we have selected a number of societies of Old World higher primates: monkeys and apes. Our choice has been determined partly by the availability of good accounts of field work – far more has been reported on these groups than on the lower primates (prosimians) or the South American monkeys – but partly also by the consideration that the apes and monkeys of the Old World are, as a group, the closest living relatives of man, and it is among them, if anywhere among subhuman primates, that we may hope to be able to determine the elements of the social organization of man's pre-human ancestor.

It is incorrect to attempt functional explanations before completing a description of, preferably, the whole of a species' behaviour, as only then would the complete range of interactions between one part of the behaviour and another be evident. But a complete description has not yet been made, for two reasons: first, each worker has his own particular interest and way of selecting information; and second, apart from the intrinsic differences of what will be presented to the worker by each species in its own setting, it is not yet clearly understood that a common framework of reference is required before comparable information from different species can be obtained. It will require special effort in observing certain species to obtain information which is evident in other species. The fact that the evidence is incomplete means that the species behaviour presented in Chapter 3 appears unsystematic.

Premature explanation in functional terms has made it difficult to see that the first step in the study of behaviour must be to discern the underlying patterns by discovering the order which holds together the separate parts of the behaviour. Most animals cannot just construct an ideal behavioural repertoire to fit the circumstances, but can only re-combine elements in their repertoire available to them from their evolutionary past. Recognition of this is accepted in studies of morphological evolution and is basic to our approach.

Much current explanation is concerned with identifying the ecological features of an environment to which a species has been adapted, and with recognizing the common features of species which inhabit similar environments. The selective pressures to which the species have been subjected can then be deduced, but these can operate to bring about a given type of behaviour only by modifying some common pre-existing structure acquired early in evolution.

We shall set out the general features of the examples already mentioned, and – by rigorously excluding the functional import of the terms used to describe behaviour – it will be seen that it is possible to derive a new and more comprehensive conceptual system for behavioural patterns. As a result it will be possible for us to see that one part of behaviour, a single act or recognizable signal, can have more than one function, and that parts of behaviour which are at present for functional reasons regarded as separate, have, nevertheless, significant interactions.

As ethology has already devised methods of observation capable of being applied to the description of the behaviour of both man and animals, we think that it is worth considering at this stage the relation of what we are attempting to do here to what social anthropologists have already begun to do in the study of human behaviour.

Biological explanations often seek to specify the need-satisfying outcomes of behaviour on the one hand and sometimes relate these supposed outcomes to explain the way in which the behaviour is adaptive. Malinowski extended this approach into human social sciences, but Durkheim, Radcliffe-Brown and Lévi-Strauss avoid the notion of purely biological function for elements of social behaviour, preferring to define their function in terms of the part they play in upholding the total social structure. Although we are, like them, concerned with revealing the total social structure, we do not use the term function to relate the parts to the whole of the structure.

One of the basic characteristics of animals as living creatures is that they behave. Behaviour is oriented in two ways; towards the physical environment – in which case the animal is reacting to an object – and towards other living animals, whether members of another species or of its own, which involves an element of reciprocity. In the animate environment, one major category of behaviour is that by which the individual relates to other members of his species. All animals display this type of behaviour to some extent, and are to that extent sociable. Such sociable interaction can take place between solitary individuals, between members of territorially separated groups, or between members of the same group. The network of such interactions constitutes the *society*.

Members of some species have a tendency to cohere, to group together for a longer or shorter period of time. One of the major contributions of ethology has been to demonstrate that the resulting groups are not simple aggregates, but are highly structured by this social network. The sociogram, or pattern of relationships between individuals, is established by assessing the degree of coherence between separate individuals in the community – that is to say, how long they persist in remaining together or how frequently they behave in particular ways towards each other. All behaviour is the result of interaction between the individual and the part of the environment significant to it. The action patterns of an individual constitute its social repertoire and reveal its hereditary propensity to behave. This behaviour may develop unaided by experience, or it may develop only if the opportunities for practice or imitation occur – a particular adult animal may never exhibit elements of behaviour for which the species as a whole has a potential.

Objects which have a significance for the animal stimulate it to action and hence are said to possess an arousal component. An animal is initially in a particular state of arousal and this, together with the arousal produced by the object, will determine the attention it pays to the stimulus object. The nature of the action which follows the arousal will be determined by the orientation component of the stimulus. In the environment at any one moment there is a pattern of stimuli, with varying degrees of significance, which comes about as a result of the obtrusiveness of any particular stimulus. There is a predisposition to act and to select any particular stimulus from the existing patterns when, for example, the animal is in a particular mood. If the arousal is high, it will bring about an overriding or persistent attention to the object.

The differential utilization of parts of the species' repertoire of behaviour brings about a distinction between the roles in the communities of different species of monkeys, often combined with differential spacing within the community. It is clearly necessary, therefore, to understand how the structure of an individual's repertoire is revealed. This is dealt with in Chapter 5.

Once this concept is grasped, it becomes clear that the structure of the individual's social repertoire gives to that individual a propensity to react with other members of the same group in such a way that its relation to them brings about the pattern of society typical of its own species. These patterns take two forms; acentric, in which the females keep separate from the males in order to disperse the components of the society, and centripetal, a rigidly structured group centred on the males. Within these two forms three types of sub-group are repeatedly encountered; female assemblies, juvenile clusters and cohorts of males (see Chapter 6). These conclusions make possible some new insights into human society. It is suggested that because human social behaviour is basically centripetal in form, in human society where institutionalized behaviour has not yet developed or where traditional social behaviour has broken down individuals have a tendency to look to and pay an excessive amount of attention to charismatic personalities. This tendency to follow such charismatic individuals appears to result from the unremitting nature of a propensity which binds our attention on to a conspicuous individual, and which we appear to have inherited from our primate ancestors. The way the different components of the society are assembled together is itself a result of the patterns of attention available to the group, and the two centripetal forms of this which can be identified are an agonistically rank-ordered form, typical of baboons and macaques, and an hedonic form, typical of the great apes.

We have set out to present the material from which these generalizations and hypotheses have been derived precisely because we want to encourage a new emphasis in the collection of data about subhuman primate societies. The new emphasis is necessary for the construction of a science of comparative social behaviour, based on the delineation of the structure of the society. Because of the inadequacy of the present methods of selection, material in Chapter 3 is presented with as little distortion of the original reports as possible, and hence appears to lack the coherence required of well marshalled evidence. Nevertheless, it enables the reader to obtain something of the flavour of the original material.

M.R.A.C.
C.J.J.

CHAPTER TWO

Introducing the Primates

WHAT IS A PRIMATE?

For as long as we have had pictorial or written records, and probably long before, men have recognized a category of creatures which were classed as animals and yet showed many of the characteristics of human beings. Travellers' tales of such beasts gave rise to myths of dog-headed men, or men with tails, or curious tribes who lived in trees and ate wood or leaves. In countries where monkeys were more familiar, their quasi-human status often ranged them with ghosts, goblins, human freaks and other anomalous beings as objects of magico-religious veneration. The same attitude persists in our own culture: the monkey house is the most popular place in any zoo and its inhabitants are regarded with a kind of fascinated disgust by human visitors.

In the works of the medieval and Renaissance natural historians we frequently find the same association between mythical-tailed races, human monsters and monkeys. The great classifiers of the seventeenth, eighteenth and early nineteenth centuries gradually eliminated the freaks and tailed men from their works, but continued to be impressed by the similarities between monkey and man. Linnaeus, the greatest of the classifiers, whose *Systema Naturae*[1] is the foundation of modern zoological classification, expressed the similarity by putting monkeys, apes, lemurs and men into a single order, Primates ('the first'). He also included other animals, such as bats, which would not now be placed in such close relationship with man, and of course a vast number of animals, both living and extinct, have been discovered and added to the order since Linnaeus' day; nevertheless, his grouping is essentially the same as that which unites man and his relatives in present-day classification.

Such classifiers as Linnaeus were concerned with putting animals into labelled categories (such as Primates), each with a number of defining characteristics shared by all its members. Linnaeus himself relied mainly on the character of the teeth; this resulted in many groupings similar to those which are still recognized, but others (such as pig, armadillo and hedgehog) which a modern classifier would call 'unnatural'.

This immediately raises the question of what is a 'natural' group? If our only concern is with putting organisms into box-like categories, we might just as well use colour of hair or shape of ears to classify them as dental characteristics, and there would be no logical reason to say that one classificatory system was any better than any other (except, of course, in such practical details as ease of application). It is really only possible to define a 'natural' classification if we accept the theory of organic evolution, which states that living species are not immutable (as Linnaeus and his predecessors and contemporaries believed), but can change over a period of time; that a species can give rise to one or more different daughter-species; and that this process of diversification can be – and has been – carried to the supra-specific levels of genus, family, order and kingdom, so that all living things are ultimately related. This theory of the mutability of species matured gradually in the thought and writings of a number of scientists over the early part of the nineteenth century, but gained its great impetus, of course, with Charles Darwin's demonstration in *The Origin of Species*[2] that the natural variability of species, combined with what he called 'natural selection', were together an intellectually adequate and scientifically elegant explanation of the mechanism by which evolution proceeded. Since Darwin's day it has been accepted more and more explicitly by animal taxonomists that a classificatory scheme should not merely convey similarities between organisms but should also express as accurately as possible their evolutionary ('phylogenetic') relationship. This is not to say that only one 'true' taxonomic scheme is possible in any animal group; merely that choice among alternative schemes must be limited to those compatible with the known events of the evolutionary history of the group. The kinds of evidence used to deduce the course which phylogeny has taken include embryology, comparative anatomy and palaeontology. Of these only the last, the study of fossils, provides

direct evidence. The evidence of comparative anatomy or embryology or living forms is of necessity indirect and inconclusive, but it
often gives plausible results when applied with caution, and many
hypotheses about phylogenetic relationships which were originally
based upon such evidence have later been confirmed by the discovery of the appropriate linking fossils.

On the whole, Linnaeus' order of Primates corresponds quite
closely with the order as it is conceived by modern taxonomists.
The classificatory scheme adopted in this book is shown on pages
210–12; this is very close to the classification of Simpson,[3] but
incorporates modifications based on new evidence.

It is usual to begin any consideration of the primates with a
'definition' of the order – a list of features by which its members are
supposedly distinguishable from those of other orders. The most
frequently quoted definition is that of Mivart:[4]

> Unguiculate, claviculate, placental mammals, with orbits
> encircled by bone; three kinds of teeth, at least at one time of
> life; brain always with a posterior lobe and calcerine fissure;
> the innermost digits of at least one pair of extremities opposable;
> hallux with a flat nail or none; a well-developed caecum; penis
> pendulous; testes scrotal; always two pectoral mammae.

Although this is probably the closest we can come to a definition
of the order, it is deficient in that most of the characteristics are
neither universally nor exclusively 'primate'; all of them appear
singly or in combination in some members of other orders. And of the
six characteristics that can be seen in the skeleton, and are hence
potentially applicable to fossil as well as extant animals, only one,
the possession of a clavicle, is universal among primates, and this is
a primitive mammalian feature only lost in animals which have
become specialized for running on all fours on the ground. We need
not, however, be too concerned about the impossibility of producing
a simple list of features by which all primates can be distinguished.
The 'definition' in this sense is a relic of pre-evolutionary, typological
thinking. All the definition we need is that primates should be a
'good' phylogenetically related group, and that this group should
contain man and his closest relatives, which are the 'type' primates.

We are then faced with the problem of how close to man an

animal must be in order to be included in the order. There is no 'right' answer to this question; the span of any taxonomic group (except, to a large extent, the species) is a matter not of biological definition but of usefulness, usage and the personal preferences of the classifier – in that order. In the case of the order Primates, various cut-off points in the evolutionary continuum have been suggested as boundaries; some have included only monkeys, apes and man, putting what we consider lower primates into a separate order. At the other extreme, other classifiers have included tree-shrews, small insect-eating mammals with little in common, superficially, even with lower primates. The view taken here is that a borderline case should be included in the order Primates if it can be shown from the fossil record to be directly related to accepted primates, and if it shows at least the beginnings of the evolutionary trends that are present in later primate groups. We should also include some primitive mammals known only as fossils which are clearly ancestors, or are very closely related to ancestors, of primates.

There are two good reasons for including these early, little-known creatures, most of which are represented only by teeth or jaw fragments and which certainly did not possess the features we would expect to see in 'typical' primates. First, we should not expect all the characteristics of a group to be present in its ancestors; if we accept the theory of evolution by gradual modification, this would be illogical. Second, to assign (as is commonly done) these basal forms to the order Insectivora, which is in effect a rag-bag of primitive placental mammals living and extinct, is not to make the best descriptive use of classification. To put them in the order Primates imparts more information about their relationships.

We have mentioned the distinctive 'trends' or paths of evolution which have been followed in the development of different primate groups. These are not defining features in the old sense, so we should not expect them to be universal within this order nor exclusive to it; they are simply features which have commonly emerged in primate evolution because of the similar response of closely related genetic heritages to common environmental situations. As far as physical features are concerned, most of the common trends of primate evolution have been well distinguished by Le Gros Clark.[5]

It is possible to distinguish an almost infinite number of structural and behavioural features which correlate functionally with the major trends of primate evolution. Here it is more instructive to group the trends into functional complexes, as in Figure 1 below. Of these, the first two complexes are probably retentions from the primitive mammalian stock; the others represent particular specializations of the primates, more highly developed in this order than in

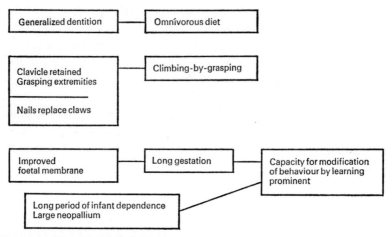

FIGURE 1: Characteristics of the primates

any other. It is interesting that these are the facets of primate adaptation which become most exaggerated in the human evolutionary line. In this sense, at least, man is the 'highest' of the primates.

THE DISTRIBUTION OF THE LIVING PRIMATES

The subhuman primates live today in Africa, Asia and South America; they retain a toehold in Europe (on Gibraltar), but are absent from North America – although the southern parts of North America were full of primates during earlier epochs. Primates had never lived in Australia before the coming of the aborigines in the geologically recent past.

Within this general range, subhuman primates are almost

entirely confined to latitudes below 35 degrees north and south, and by far the majority of species are confined to the tropics. As might be expected in such a tree-loving group, the tropical evergreen forests of the Old and New Worlds, with their variety of arboreal habitats, are the areas richest in primate fauna in terms both of numbers of individuals and of species, but other tropical habitats, such as grasslands, savannahs, scrub country and monsoon forests, are also widely exploited by non-human primates.

A few species, all belonging to the Cercopithecoidea (Old World monkeys), extend into warm or cool temperate regions, and others of the same group extend into high mountain country in the Himalayas.

Although we are accustomed to think of them as warm-climate animals, the non-human primates are not confined to low latitudes by an inability to adapt to cold conditions. Some monkey species thrive in the severe conditions of winter on the Tibetan plateau, in the Himalayas or in northern China. Monkeys from tropical Africa have been kept in outdoor cages throughout Moscow winters, after appropriate acclimatization, during which they grew exceptionally dense, furry coats. The decisive factor confining subhuman primates to low latitudes is probably their dependence upon vision as their dominant sense. Mammals which rely more upon scent than vision to find their food can forage as well in twilight or dark as in daylight, and are little inconvenienced by the short winter days or the short summer nights of high latitudes. This gives them a considerable advantage over the vision-dependent primates under such conditions.

The nature of vision is such that a highly acute eye must be adapted to function in either strong or weak light. The nocturnally adapted primates, like bushbabies and pottos, hide their sensitive eyes during strong daylight; if they are prevented from doing this, serious inflammation results. Monkeys, apes and most larger Madagascar lemurs, on the other hand, have acute diurnal vision but are virtually blind after nightfall and would soon fall prey to nocturnal predators if they left their inaccessible sleeping perches on trees or rocks. These patterns of behaviour work well in the tropics, where day and night are of approximately equal length throughout the year and the daily transition from daylight to dark is rapid. At latitude 50 degrees, however, a diurnally adapted primate would have only eight hours to forage on a midwinter day and this is the 'leanest' season when food would be most difficult to find. Under such conditions it might well be impossible for the animal to maintain its body temperature and hence to survive. At the same latitude a nocturnally adapted prosimian would have only seven hours of foraging between sunset and sunrise in midsummer and hence would be at a severe disadvantage compared with smell-oriented animals like rodents.

THE MAIN DIVISIONS OF LIVING PRIMATES

It is convenient to describe the living primates in terms of the families among which the taxonomists divide them. Most of these are rather distinct and clear-cut groups. Of the families to be described the first six comprise the sub-order Prosimii, often called 'lower primates', in which, on the whole, the distinctively primate features are less developed than in the other sub-order, the Anthropoidea. The other groupings, which include the primate families, are indicated in the classificatory table.

Tree-shrews (Tupaiidae)

This is a group of small, active animals of rather squirrel-like appearance, although their elongated snouts are more reminiscent of insectivorous animals such as moles. They are widely distributed in South East Asia. Thirteen species are currently recognized, grouped into five genera. One species, the pen-tailed tree-shrew (*Ptilocercus lowei*), appears distinct from the rest and is put into a sub-family of its own. Little is known of the natural history of wild tree-shrews. They are found in tropical forests or bush country, where they live in the trees, in the shrub layer or even on the ground, according to species. Most reports indicate that they are 'soft food omnivores'; they will eat soft fruits and vegetables and have a distinct liking for insects and small vertebrates.

Although some anatomical features of the tree-shrews recall the prosimian primates, especially the lemurs of Madagascar, others, such as the clawed digits, are unlike those of other primates, and for

26

this reason some authorities would exclude them from the primates completely. Whether or not we include them in the order, they are of interest to the primatologist as being the nearest approach, among living animals, to the pre-primates from which the order was ultimately derived.

Madagascar lemurs (Lemuridae, Indriidae and Daubentoniidae)

Madagascar has been isolated from the mainland of Africa since before the emergence of most modern types of mammals, and its fauna is a unique assortment of animals which have managed, at various times, to cross by the 'sweepstake route' of rafting on floating masses of vegetation. Many of these are rather primitive types which have survived in the refuge of Madagascar but have become extinct in their original African homes. At some time during the early Tertiary period the island was colonized by prosimian primates. Probably this event occurred in the Eocene, when prosimians were widespread, diverse and numerous and the higher primates (Anthropoidea) had yet to emerge. The colonists would have numbered only a few individuals, and in all probability represented only one species. From this beginning the prosimian stock on Madagascar speciated and diversified by the process of adaptive radiation until, at its peak and before the coming of man to the island, it comprised about seventeen genera, ranging in size from animals as large as a chimpanzee to others as small as a dormouse. The lemur fauna of Madagascar today is an impoverished relic of this rich radiation; with the coming of man and his domestic animals the larger, slower lemurs and those which were ground adapted and therefore less able to escape into the trees have disappeared, leaving only the smaller, more agile and mainly more primitive forms. Even these are now threatened with extinction in many parts of their range.

In many ways the Madagascan lemurs as a group have departed less from the primitive mammalian structure than any other living primate group, with the exception of the tree-shrews. They have pointed, muzzled faces, rather like those of small dogs, cats or rodents. The presence of tactile whiskers (vibrissae) and a moist, naked 'dog's nose' (rhinarium) increases their 'bestial' appearance in contrast to the far more human-like Anthropoidea. Although

27

sight is probably the dominant sense in all Madagascar lemurs, scent is still important and many lemurs use scent glands in communication. Although relatively larger than that of most non-primate mammals, the brain of the lemur is still small compared with that of the Anthropoidea.

On the other hand, almost all the lemurs have the features associated with the primate pattern of 'climbing by grasping' – the nails on all digits (except the second one of the foot, which retains a claw for grooming the fur), the well-developed and divergent big toe and thumb.

Of all the living Madagascar primates the most peculiar is the aye-aye (*Daubentonia*); so peculiar indeed that it is given its own family and super-family by most classifiers. Alone of the lemurs it has claws on all its digits apart from the hallux (big toe). Its middle finger is a twig-like, attenuated structure and its brain shows a most unprimate pattern of grooves and ridges. Its dentition is perhaps its most strikingly aberrant feature. Like the rodents, the aye-aye has lost its canine teeth, both top and bottom, as well as most of its premolars, leaving a broad diastema or gap between the incisors and the remaining cheek-teeth. The incisors themselves are extremely strong and chisel-like and, like those of the rodents, grow continuously throughout their life. The cheek-teeth, on the other hand, are very weak and adapted to eating only the softest food. Peculiar as it is, there is little doubt that the aye-aye is an offshoot of the main group of Madagascar lemurs. All its dental peculiarities can be related to its rather specialized way of life; it feeds almost exclusively upon the soft-bodied grubs of wood-boring insects, which it extracts from their tunnels by using its strong incisors and elongated, clawed middle finger. It is interesting that the very same pattern of behaviour is seen in an Australian marsupial, where it is associated with exactly similar physical specializations, down to the elongated finger: a nice example of convergent evolution at work!

The two remaining families of Madagascar lemurs are separated by their dental formulae: the Lemuridae have three premolars, the Indriidae have only two and have lost their lower canine. The living Indriidae are a closely-related group. All are medium-to-large, lanky animals, highly arboreal, feeding mainly on foliage, buds and the bark of trees. They are prodigious leapers and prefer to rest upon vertical supports, especially the trunks of trees, to which they cling with their pincer-like hands and feet, their long powerful legs drawn closely up to the body. Of the three genera two (*Indri* and *Propithecus*) are diurnal in behaviour, the other (*Lichanotus*) is nocturnal.

The other family of Madagascar lemurs, the Lemuridae, is a rather heterogeneous group and is divided into five sub-families, of which only two survive. Among the extinct Lemuridae are *Megaladapis*, a large, bulky, slow, climbing animal, which probably looked rather like a koala in life, and other animals which had a rather monkey-like appearance and probably lived on the ground – prosimian equivalents to the baboons. Of the two living sub-families, the Cheirogaleinae are small, furry, nocturnal animals, ranging from dormouse to kitten size; they seem to be 'soft food omnivores', and consume a large number of insects. In many features the Cheirogaleinae are, as a group, the most primitive of the Madagascar lemurs; the original invaders of the island may well have been small animals resembling the mouse-lemur *Microcebus*.

The other sub-family of the Lemuridae includes the genus *Lemur* itself, the so-called 'typical' lemurs. In some ways the genus *Lemur* is less typical of the Madagascar lemurs as a group than is often implied in textbooks. It is, for instance, the only genus which has the extremely long, 'foxy' muzzle which is often portrayed as representative of all Lemuridae, or even of all prosimians. All species of *Lemur* are diurnally active, gregarious, medium-sized animals, many of which have fur with striking colour patterns. They are predominantly fruit eaters and live for the most part in trees. The best-known species is *L. catta*, the ringtailed lemur, a familiar zoo animal. A second genus of the Lemurinae, *Lepilemur*, has habits more like the Indriidae; it is a nocturnal form, a 'clinger and leaper' and a foliage eater. The remaining genus of the Lemurinae (*Hapalemur*) is little known. At least one form is a reed-eating animal confined to the margins of Lake Aloatra in central Madagascar.

Galagos, lorises and pottos (Lorisidae)

The species of this family live in mainland Africa (galagos and potto) and South East Asia (lorises). All are small to medium-sized, arboreal, nocturnal, furry primates, but may be divided into two sub-families which differ in their way of life and hence in a cluster of related structural features. A number of features of this family are shared with the Madagascar lemurs: their pointed faces with a rhinarium; moderate brain size; and grasping hands and feet, equipped with nails except for the second toe of the foot. From details of skull structure, however, it is clear that the two groups are separate; possibly the Lorisidae are the descendants of an ancient African or Asiatic prosimian group, separate from that to which the original lemur colonists of Madagascar belonged.

The first sub-family, Galaginae, is entirely African and includes probably only a single valid genus, *Galago.* Galagos are the bush-babies familiar as pets, varying from cat to rat size. Externally the most striking features of galagos are their large, rather prominent eyes, big ears, long tails and proportionally very long hind limbs. Their vision and hearing are well adapted to nocturnal insect-hunting, while their long hind limbs enable them to make rapid leaps from branch to branch, either in pursuit of their prey or to escape from predators. Galagos spend the day hiding either in a nest of leaves or in a hollow tree (according to species). Most are forest dwellers, but the two most widespread species (*G. crassi-caudatus* and *G. senegalensis*) occur in quite arid acacia savannah.

The Lorisinae include several genera. The potto and angwantibo (*Perodicticus* and *Arctocebus* respectively) are African and inhabit parts of the great Congo-Cameroons forest belt. The lorises (*Loris* and *Nycticebus*) live in the forests of South East Asia. All the Lorisinae have a very distinctive way of moving – a sinuous walk, deliberate rather than slow, in which at least two extremities, and usually three, are firmly gripping the branch at any time. As adaptations to this locomotor pattern Lorisinae have rather long lumbar regions, powerful, pincer-like hands and feet, in which the second digits are more or less reduced, and fore and hind limbs of approximately equal length. They also have smaller ears than the galagos, though they share with them the large eyes of nocturnal animals. There are striking differences between the various Lorisinae in body-build. The potto is a rather tubby-looking, stoutly built animal. The angwantibo and slow loris (*Nycticebus*) are somewhat slimmer, while the slender loris (*Loris*) is the slenderest of all, with skinny, twig-like limbs.

The preferred diet of all Lorisinae seems to be insects, small

30

vertebrates and soft fruits, the most consistently carnivorous and insectivorous genus being *Loris*. Pottos, angwantibos and lorises have been reported as eating birds; the stealthy locomotion and ability to move along slender twigs may well be an adaptation to stalking roosting birds as well as large insects. Although very little is known yet about the habits of Lorisinae in the wild, the indications are that they are not sociable animals.

Tarsier (Tarsiidae)

This family has only one living genus, *Tarsius*, the tarsier, and this is confined to forests in some of the islands of the East Indies. In appearance the tarsier is not unlike a small bushbaby in which the characteristic 'galago' features have been greatly exaggerated; it has large ears, a short but pointed snout and relatively enormous eyes. Its hind limbs are greatly elongated, and both hands and feet are long-fingered and terminate in flattened pads for grasping, some-what like those of a tree-frog. The tail is long. The animal is nocturnal and progresses by a series of rather frog-like hops and leaps from stem to stem. The food of tarsiers in the wild is thought to consist largely of insects and small vertebrates. Although superficially like a bushbaby, many structural features of the tarsier show it to be of quite distinct stock. For instance, the rhinarium is absent, the tooth structure is quite different and grooming claws are present on both second and third pedal digits. The fossil record suggests that the tarsier has descended separate and almost unchanged from the Eocene era, perhaps fifty million years ago.

New World monkeys (Cebidae and Callithrichidae)

With these two families we enter the second major division of the order, the Anthropoidea or higher primates. The group as a whole has certain features which distinguish it from the Prosimii: an increased dependence upon vision and a regression of olfaction; absence of grooming claws and, most important and fundamental, a great increase in relative brain size.

In spite of these similarities, shared by all Anthropoidea, it is clear that they fall into two major groupings which have only a remote phylogenetic connection, and may, in fact, be descended from different prosimian groups. These major groupings correspond to the geographical division between Old and New World Anthropoidea.

The New World primates are all highly arboreal animals, confined to the tropical forests of South and Central America. They fall into two groups: the Callithrichidae and the Cebidae.

The Callithrichidae are the marmosets and tamarins which are familiar as zoo animals and popular pets. They are miniature monkeys, distinguished from all other Anthropoidea by the possession of claws on all their digits apart from the big toe. Many species are decorated with coloured patches or tufts of fur. Like almost all Anthropoidea, marmosets are diurnal animals. Their claws enable them to climb tree trunks and branches in much the same way as a squirrel. The marmosets have the generalized primate dietary habit: they eat insects, small vertebrates and forest fruits.

The Cebidae are a larger and more diverse family. All members are distinguished from the marmosets by their larger size, by the possession of nails (albeit rather compressed ones) on all digits, and by their dentition, which includes three molar teeth. Almost all the marmosets have lost their third (hindmost) molar, presumably in relation to a general reduction in jaw size.

Some of the Cebidae are so like Old World monkeys in external appearance that it is difficult to believe that their relationship is distant. However, the structure of their skull and teeth is quite different; in particular, the South American monkeys have three premolars to the Old World monkeys' two, and the structure of the bulla, the bony capsule containing the internal ear, is completely distinct. The living animals can often be told apart by the breadth of the nose; in the South American monkeys the nostrils are as a rule more widely spaced than in the Old World monkeys, and face sideways rather than forwards or downwards. Some other features may be a guide to Old or New World provenance: some Cebidae – but not all – have prehensile tails, capable of acting as a grasping organ; no Cercopithecoidea (Old World monkeys) have these. On the other hand, some Old World – but no New World – monkeys have pouches in their cheeks for the temporary storage of food. Finally, all Cercopithecoidea – but no Platyrrhini – have bare sitting pads on their posteriors.

The most primitive of the Cebidae are the titis (*Callicebus*), small, rather marmoset-like monkeys which have thickly haired and non-prehensile tails. They run and leap on all fours in the higher branches of forest trees.

The squirrel monkeys (*Saimiri*) are also small, arboreal quadrupeds with long and thickly haired tails used as balancers in leaping. The last member of this rather primitive group is the night-monkey (*Aotes*), an animal that is unique among the Anthropoidea in being adapted to nocturnal life; its enormous eyes are the most obvious signs of this adaptation.

The remaining Cebidae have departed from the locomotor pattern and body form seen in the smaller and more primitive members of the family and have all become to some extent deliberate climbers rather than quadrupedal leapers and runners. The Pitheciinae (*Cacajao*, *Pithecia* and *Chiropotes*) are a rather distinct sub-family; all of them have non-prehensile tails and often long or shaggy fur. The capuchin monkeys (*Cebus*) are perhaps the most familiar of New World monkeys. They are small to medium-sized animals with prehensile tails which they carry curled like a watch-spring. The spider monkeys (*Atelinae*) have carried the locomotor tendency towards deliberate climbing still further and have become arm-swingers or brachiators, i.e. they swing hand-over-hand below the branch. This had led to a number of anatomical peculiarities: the limbs, especially the arms, are elongated and the hand forms a hook; the thumb is absent externally and the long, prehensile tail acts as a fifth limb.

The howler monkeys (*Alouatta*) are deliberate climbers rather than brachiators and have the distinction of being the only New World primates whose social organization has been extensively studied in the wild. Their name is derived from the powerful voice of the adult males, which is produced by a unique and highly developed vocal apparatus and is apparently used as a form of territorial defence against other howler troops.

Very little is known about the natural history of the Cebidae; one would expect that such a diverse group would show a great variety of ecological adaptations, but few details emerge from available accounts. Such information as we have suggests that all Cebidae feed on young leaves, forest fruits and occasional animal food such as insects.

c

Old World monkeys (Cercopithecidae)

This family includes all the familiar tailed monkeys of the Old World tropics. It is, currently, by far the most widespread and successful group of the Old World primates, both in number of species and, with the exception of man, in number of individuals. Because the great majority of primate species whose social organization has been studied belong to this family, it will be given rather more detailed consideration here than the preceding groups.

The family is divisible into two distinct sub-families, which some classifiers would give the rank of full family. The more familiar of these is Cercopithecinae.

The Cercopithecinae are a widespread and diverse group which lives in an enormous variety of habitats, ranging from tropical rain forest to the bleak Tibetan plateau. Yet their physical structure, and still more their biochemical similarities, indicate that they are a group which has undergone extensive evolutionary radiation only relatively recently. Various lines of evidence suggest that this radiation occurred during the Pliocene period, and in trans-Saharan Africa.

All the Cercopithecinae are quadrupeds, and most spend at least part of their time on the ground. Perhaps closest to the ancestral Cercopithecinae are the guenons (*Cercopithecus*). These are small to medium-sized African monkeys of which the most familiar example is perhaps the vervet (*Cercopithecus aethiops*), a species frequently seen in zoos or as a pet. The taxonomy of the guenons is still, in spite of a wealth of museum material and several Herculean attempts at synthesis, in an unsatisfactory state. Practically every African forest contains several species of arboreal guenon, and each population has its own particular pattern of hair-tufts and coloured markings in the fur. These have presumably evolved as species-recognition features, and parallel and convergent evolution of similar patterns must have occurred many times in different areas. Very little is known as yet about the range of behavioural variation which accompanies this great physical variability.

For our purposes the guenons can be divided quite simply into two main groups, according to their habitat. *Cercopithecus aethiops*, the vervet monkey and its relatives, is an animal of wooded savannah and riverside forest strips. It is distributed throughout trans-Saharan Africa wherever this habitat is present, and is the commonest monkey in many regions. The remaining *Cercopithecus* species are forest animals; some have a broad distribution, others are limited to quite small areas. Only two species have been extensively studied in the wild, *Cercopithecus mitis*, a species which occurs in much of East, Central and South Africa under a variety of common names (Sykes's monkey, blue monkey, golden monkey, samango monkey, etc.), and *C. ascanius*, the redtail or coppertail monkey, a species confined to the Congo forest region. The patas or hussar monkey (*Erythrocebus patas*) is a close relative of the guenons (some would put it in the same genus) which has taken to life in open country and has become adapted accordingly, both physically and in its social structures.

The second group of monkeys within the sub-family Cercopithe-cinae consists of the macaques (*Macaca*), mangabeys (*Cercocebus*), common baboons (*Papio*) and mandrills (*Mandrillus*). The macaques are the only extant Cercopithecinae which live outside the Ethiopian faunal zone. Most of the species are Asiatic and live in India and the Far East. One, the Barbary ape (*M. sylvana*), is now found in Morocco and Gibraltar only; it is probably the European representative of the genus which was expelled from Europe by glacial conditions during the Pleistocene period. It occurs in interglacial deposits as far north as England, and survived into the early post-Pleistocene in Sardinia.

Most macaques are rather nondescript animals; they lack the brightly coloured fur of other monkeys, and the species are distin-guished externally by differences in tail-length and by patterns of hair-growth rather than by colour. Today many macaques live in almost treeless conditions, often around human dwellings, and spend most of their foraging time on the ground. This has led some authors to assume that they are basically ground-adapted animals, the equivalent of the baboons of Africa. We have to remember, however, that the habitat of these monkeys in East Asia and the Mediter-ranean littoral has been profoundly modified by human agriculture in the very recent past. But for this modification, most of India would be covered by monsoon forest, South China by sub-tropical or warm-temperate rain forest, and the Mediterranean coast by evergreen woodland. Under such conditions the macaques would have found part of their food on the ground but most of it in the trees, just as they do today in the less disturbed rain forests of South East Asia and temperate mixed forest of Japan. The limb structure of the macaques bears this out; it clearly indicates adaptation to a semi-arboreal way of life, and lacks the more extreme adaptations to ground-living seen in the true baboons. Unfortunately, because it is easier and more convenient to watch monkeys which live in close association with man in bazaars, temples and roadside trees in agricultural land, most of our information on the social organization of 'wild' macaques was gathered under such unnatural conditions.

Although several rather different kinds of macaques can be distinguished, it is by no means clear on present evidence where the lines between species and species-groups should be drawn. A survey of the taxonomy of the group is now in progress and should clarify the position considerably. It is already clear that the idea implied by extremist 'lumpers' that the macaques are a single polytypic species is incorrect. In this account we will use the names that are generally current, with the proviso that some of these may have to be combined in single species in the final analysis.

The rhesus monkey (*M. mulatta*) is perhaps the most familiar macaque. It is the traditional laboratory primate and as such is the subject of a vast literature. Its many described races have a total range from West Pakistan to Central China, extending northwards to Tibet and southwards to Central India. To the south the rhesus is replaced by two other species with longer tails; in South India and Ceylon by the bonnet macaques (*M. radiata*) and in Indo-China, Thailand, Malaya and some of the East Indian Islands by the crab-eating or kraa monkey (*M. fascicularis*) often called *M. irus*. There is some evidence that the latter, at least, may be conspecific with the rhesus monkey. The Formosan macaque is almost certainly a race of the rhesus. The pigtailed macaque (*M. nemestrina*) is a rather distinct species which overlaps with *M. fascicularis* over much of its range. Another distinctive species is the wanderoo or lion-tailed macaque (*M. silenus*), a rain-forest animal confined to extreme south-west India.

Another distinct group of macaques (the grouping is a useful mental pigeon-hole at least; whether it is natural has yet to be established) are those with little or no external tail. These are the Barbary ape (*M. sylvana*) of the Maghreb and Gibraltar, the Japanese macaque, confined to the more southerly of the Japanese islands, and the red-faced or bear macaque of Burma, Thailand and parts of northern Indo-China. Each of these is probably a distinct species. The macaques which are found only on the island of Celebes are something of a puzzle. Two types have usually been distinguished; the black ape and the Moor macaque. These are both black, stump-tailed animals, but the black ape has a peculiarly elongated and ridged muzzle which gives it a superficial resemblance to some of the baboons (*Papio*). It has generally been placed in a genus (*Cynopithecus*) separate from the macaques on this account. Yet the two forms are closely alike in other ways (indeed, the juveniles are indistinguishable), and, still more significant, intermediates between them have been described from the wild. It therefore seems more logical to suggest that they are close relatives, probably sub-species of a single species, one of which has acquired a peculiar muzzle form. There is really no reason why such a feature should not be developed as a sub-specific character as easily as a peculiar pelage pattern or a reduction in tail length, yet such is the reverence for the skull (and still more the dentition) among taxonomists that any aberrant characteristic in this part is given excessive weight in taxonomic judgments.

The African genera *Papio* and *Mandrillus* are now considered closely related and there might be a case for combining them in a single genus with *Cercocebus* as there is no good reason, on present evidence, to combine *Papio* and *Mandrillus* but leave the mangabeys out. The mangabeys are all forest-living, African monkeys. On ecological grounds they seem to fall into two rather distinct groups. The black mangabeys (*Cercocebus aterrimus* and *C. albigena*) are highly arboreally-adapted animals which scarcely ever leave the trees, although they have on rare occasions been observed crop-raiding. The two species are distinguished by the pattern of growth of the long, silky black hair. The remaining mangabeys (it is uncertain how many species should be distinguished) appear from available accounts to spend a good deal of their time foraging on the forest floor, as well as in the trees. The structure of their limbs bears this out.

We have very little information on the natural history of social organization of this most interesting group; the only member to have been studied from this point of view is the grey-cheeked mangabey (*Cercocebus albigena*), one of the more arboreal species.

Baboons of the genus *Papio* are the most widespread of the African monkeys; they are found in all areas south of the Sahara apart from waterless deserts and flat, treeless grasslands, and one species extends beyond Africa into south-west Arabia. Baboons of this genus are the largest living primates, with the exception of the great apes and man. There is a rather marked difference in size between the sexes, the male being up to twice the weight of the female, which is probably correlated with the role of the male as defender of the group against the many predators found in the open-country habitat. There is also, for the same reason, a difference between the sexes in the structure of the canine teeth: in the male these are powerful, sabre-like weapons; in the female they scarcely project beyond the incisors. This sexual difference is seen in most species of monkeys, but is most pronounced in the baboons.

Papio baboons are mainly vegetarian; their diet varies widely according to habitat, but fruits, seeds, grass and roots are all eaten. Insects and small animals are often eaten when they are available, and occasionally baboons in an area will take to killing and eating the young of larger animals such as sheep or antelopes. Although the baboons (together with the patas monkey) are the only monkeys which are physically adapted to a life spent mainly on the ground, and hence are able to range into more open country than other species, many baboon groups can and do live in woodland or forest areas where most of their food is fruit gathered in the trees. These are the so-called forest baboons, which are not a taxonomic group but simply local groups of quite widespread baboon species which happen to live in forests.

The taxonomy of the genus *Papio* is still disputed. It falls quite clearly into two major groups. The first of these contains only the hamadryas baboon (*Papio hamadryas*), a species confined to arid vegetational zones (mainly semi-desert scrub) in eastern Ethiopia, Somalia, and the adjacent coast of southern Arabia. The exigencies of this harsh environment have led to adaptations of the social organization of the hamadryas, and, in turn, to physical peculiarities correlated with this social organization, as is explained in a later section.

The other division of the genus contains all the other forms of *Papio*. These are called 'savannah baboons', an inappropriate title as they live in every available habitat from semi-desert scrub to evergreen rain forest as well as savannah. This division of the genus, under the general name of *P. cynocephalus*, falls into four sections, which traditionally have been called species: *Papio ursinus* (the chacma and Rhodesian baboons), *P. anubis* (the olive, anubis or doguera baboon), *P. papio* (the Guinea baboon) and *P. cynocephalus* (the yellow baboon). Each of these is a physically distinct type, and each varies internally, especially in size. Should they be called species or sub-species? Much hot air and dogmatism have been expended on this question, but the answer must be that we simply do not yet have the crucial information about the amount of contact that exists in nature between these populations, and how far gene-flow between them is restricted by biological factors when such contact occurs. It is true that populations of *Papio* replace each other geographically; this is a necessary characteristic of sub-species of the same species, but good species, or even genera, can also replace each other geographically if they are closely equivalent in ecology.

There is some evidence that forms intermediate between the yellow and chacma baboons occur at one end of their zone of contact, yet that the two forms elsewhere live side by side without interbreeding. The same may be true of the olive and yellow baboons. There is no evidence of intergradation between olive and Guinea baboons, but the crucial areas have not been well explored. On present evidence a case could be made for either specific or sub-specific rank for the major populations of 'savannah' baboons. The important thing is that the controversy over taxonomy and nomenclature should not obscure the fact that the genetical and breeding structure of this group of baboons is likely to be at an intermediate and very interesting stage between sub-speciation and speciation.

We suggest a classification which retains full specific rank for *ursinus*, *anubis*, *papio* and *cynocephalus* but combines them in a single superspecies *Papio cynocephalus* supersp. In this way we express the diversity of the group, but also its rather close relationship and its separateness from *P. hamadryas*, which is excluded from the superspecies. It also gives us a convenient 'scientific' synonym of 'savannah' baboon as that term is generally used.

The genus *Papio* has been more widely studied in the wild than most of the primates: accounts have been published of the social behaviour of the anubis, yellow and chacma baboons (all members of the *P. cynocephalus* group), and of the hamadryas. It is clear, how-ever, that the behaviour of baboons varies enormously from place to place, according to habitat, and there is undoubtedly much to learn before the breadth of behavioural diversity within the genus is fully described. As with macaques, attention has been focused mainly on groups of baboons which live in rather open country where observation is easier: social organization has been found to be different in populations even of the same species which live in more wooded areas.

The drill and mandrill (*Madrillus leucophaeus* and *M. sphinx*) are large baboon-like animals which inhabit the westerly parts of the Congo-Cameroon forest region. Their ranges are slightly different, but overlap, and they are almost certainly to be regarded as a good species. Their most striking features, which are more highly developed in the adult male, are the facial ridges and brightly coloured skin of the posterior. In the mandrill, the facial bosses are especially massive and are coloured, sky-blue, contrasting with the bright red nasal stripe between them. In the drill the face is plain black. Very little is known about either the natural history or the social organization of these two species. They are generally said to be animals of the forest floor, but their limb structure suggests that they do more tree-climbing than baboons of the genus *Papio*, though less than the mangabeys.

A most interesting animal is the gelada baboon (*Theropithecus gelada*), a species confined to the country above the tree-line on the high plateau of central Ethiopia. It is a baboon only by virtue of its long face and ground-living habits, and its relationship to *Papio* is not very close. It is in fact the last survivor of a group of monkeys very highly specialized for life on the ground which flourished over most of Africa up until the beginning of the Upper Pleistocene, only about sixty thousand years ago, when they disappear from fossil record, probably due to human predation and competition. Among them are the famous 'giant' baboons of Olduvai and other Early and Middle Pleistocene sites. Their dentition suggests that they were largely grass eaters, as is the gelada still. The gelada is an impressive animal, with its magnificent cape of golden brown fur, deep black face with the peculiar prominent but snub nose and, most peculiar of all, the patch of naked skin on the breast. This is larger in females and varies in colour according to the state of the sexual cycle of the animal.

The second sub-family of the Cercopithecidae is the Colobinae. The monkeys of this group are leaf eaters rather than omnivores like the Cercopithecinae. They lack the cheek-pouches of the latter sub-family, but instead have a large stomach whose capacity is increased by sacculation, enabling them rapidly to gather and eat quantities of leaves. It has been suggested that the earliest Cercopithecinae were probably leaf eaters like the living Colobinae, which therefore represent a primitive stock from which the Cercopithecinae are a relatively recent offshoot. Compared to the Cercopithecinae the Colobinae are more equally distributed between Asia and Africa, with a predominance in number of genera and species in the former continent.

All the Colobinae are rather highly adapted to an arboreal way of life. The majority of them are active leapers, though without the extreme specializations for this locomotor habit seen in some of the prosimians. In all, the fingers are long and the thumb somewhat reduced; this reaches its highest development in *Colobus*, in which the external thumb is generally absent.

The only member of the Colobinae found in Africa is the genus *Colobus*, the guereza or colobus monkey. Of these, the best known is the spectacular black-and-white colobus, which exists in many varieties throughout the tropical-forest belt of Central and West Africa, and also in many of the patches of montane forest. As is the case in so many primate groups, it is uncertain just how many species should be distinguished among the black-and-white colobus. Quite possibly they should all be put into a single polytypic species. A second major group within the genus includes the so-called 'red' colobus. These occur over much the same area as the black-and-white group, but are rather less widespread. The third group contains only the olive colobus, a small and rather secretive species that is found only in parts of the West African forest belt. Some information is available about the natural history of the olive and the black-and-white colobus, but no studies in depth of their social organization have been reported.

The Asiatic Colobinae are a more varied group. Their range is centred upon the tropical rain forests of South East Asia, but extends into monsoon (deciduous) forest, montane forests in the Himalayas and sub-tropical and warm-temperate rain forests in South China. Most of the Asiatic Colobinae can be put into the genus *Presbytis*, which some authors would subdivide. The rain forest forms of the genus, like those of *Cercopithecus*, are a bewildering array which have yet to be definitely revised. The monsoon-forest forms can probably all be put into a single species, the so-called common or hanuman langur, *Presbytis entellus*. Living naturally in a more open habitat than the rain-forest langurs, this species has probably always had to use terrestrial pathways between the trees in which it feeds. This has enabled it to survive, like the macaques, in parts of India where human activity has removed both most of the forest cover and most of the monkeys' natural predators. The rather high degree of terrestrial activity observed in such regions must be regarded as artificial, if only because the limb structure of the langur is tree-adapted. The common langur is the only member of the Colobinae whose social structure has been extensively studied, and the greater part of this study was carried out in an agricultural area.

The douc langur is a rather distinct form that is usually put into a separate genus, *Pygathrix*. It is found only in parts of Indo-China, and no study of its social organization has been published.

The remaining members of the Asiatic Colobinae are all distinguished by having rather peculiar external noses, and are all found in areas peripheral to the main langur habitat. *Simias*, the Pagai Island langur, is a little-known form apparently confined to some islands off the coast of Sumatra. *Nasalis*, the proboscis monkey, which is confined to the island of Borneo, is remarkable for the great development of the external nose, especially in the male, in which it is long and pendulous. Another distinction of the proboscis monkey is its high degree of sexual dimorphism in size; the male is larger relative to the female than in practically any other monkey species. Great sexual dimorphism in monkeys is generally associated with ground-living and the special role of the adult male as defender of the group against predators under the dangerous conditions of terrestrial life. It will be interesting to discover the function of extreme dimorphism in the highly arboreal proboscis monkey, but the necessary field studies have yet to be made. Another peripheral form with an odd nose, this time a retroussé one, is the snub-nosed monkey of south-western China (*Rhinopithecus*). Its habits and social organization are unknown.

It will be appreciated from this necessarily brief and sketchy account of the family that the Cercopithecidae are a diverse group; the full extent of this diversity is often not fully appreciated by those who make generalizations about 'monkey behaviour'. Another point worth noting is that although most of the detailed studies of primate social organization have been made on Old World monkeys, the majority of species, indeed whole genera, remain uninvestigated.

Gibbons (Hylobatidae)

With the gibbons we come to the members of the superfamily to which man belongs, the Hominoidea. The most obvious common features of the living members of the superfamily are the relatively great brain-size (greater than in monkeys, either New or Old World) and absence of a tail. The structure of their molar teeth is different from that of Old World monkeys, though their dental formula is the same. Serological studies support the view that the Hominoidea are a natural group, that is, they are descended from a common ancestor not shared with any other extant group.

The gibbons themselves are small to medium-sized highly arboreal primates which live in the rain forests of South East Asia. Their most striking feature is their enormously long arms and hands. These are an adaptation to the gibbons' locomotory speciality. Gibbons never progress through the trees on all fours as do, for instance, monkeys. They either walk upright along branches on their hind legs, often with their arms outstretched in much the same way as a tight-rope walker uses his pole, or, more commonly, they swing hand over hand below the branch with their feet and legs tucked up beneath them. This is the mode of progression known as 'brachiation'; it is in the locomotory repertoire of most arboreal primates; some, like the spider monkeys of South America, use it regularly, but the gibbon is the most regular, agile and specialized brachiator. As well as the more obvious features of the hands and arms associated with habitual arm-swinging, other characteristics of gibbon anatomy can be correlated functionally with brachiation. These include a rib-cage

43

that is flattened from front to back, rather than from side to side as in the quadrupeds, a scapula with a long vertebral border, and a short lumbar region.

Because these brachiator characteristics are shared to some extent with the great apes (chimp, gorilla and orang-utan) some would argue that the gibbons should not be given separate family status. This view has little to recommend it. It is clear from the fossil record and the indirect evidence of serology that the gibbons split from the common ancestral stock of the Hominoidea very early in its history, probably before the line leading to man became distinct. If we allot the Hominidae to a separate family there is good reason to separate the gibbons at this level. However, taxonomic practice does not make this obligatory as long as the common features of gibbons and great apes which distinguish them from Hominidae are true relicts from the ancestral condition; in this case we could classify living apes, gibbons and ancestral Hominoids all as Pongidae, with the Hominidae a separate family because of their radical departure from the ancestral form. This is not the situation in the Hominoidea. The gibbons and great apes, in acquiring brachiating specializations, have probably departed as much from the ancestral hominoid structure as has bipedal man. More important, they acquired the habit of brachiation and associated characteristics independently of each other, just as did some of the New World monkeys and at least two other primate lines now extinct. Such characters are clearly very poor indicators of taxonomic affinity.

The gibbons are commonly divided into two genera: *Symphalangus*, with only one species (*S. syndactylus*), the large siamang of Sumatra; and *Hylobates*, the true gibbon with a number of species that still needs to be determined exactly. Generic separation between these two may well be unjustified. Only *Hylobates* and only one species (*H. lar*) of this genus, has been studied in the wild. Its diet appears to be rather similar to that of the *Cercopithecus* monkeys of African forests, which are probably its ecological replacement; it lives mainly on fruit, with some leaves and a few insects and young birds.

Great apes (Pongidae)

This group of subhuman primates needs little introduction, since all its members are familiar inhabitants of zoological gardens.

Current taxonomic opinion inclines to divide it into only two genera, which have evidently been separated for a considerable period. One (*Pan*) is entirely African, the other (*Pongo*) is entirely Asiatic.

As a group, the Pongidae are Hominoidea, distinguished from the gibbons by their tooth structure, the shape of their hands and the general absence of 'sitting-pads'. The Pongidae all build tree-beds in which they spend the night. They are distinguished from Hominidae by absence of that complex of features in the skull, teeth and postcranial skeleton which are associated with the hominid adaptation: terrestrial bipedalism with dependence upon tool-using.

The African Pongidae are the gorilla (*Pan gorilla*) and the chimpanzee (*Pan troglodytes*). The pygmy chimpanzee shares different characteristics with each of the two species, and may well rank as a third (*Pan paniscus*). On the other hand, it may be no more than a race of the common chimpanzee. Its range, entirely within western Africa south of the Congo river, does not overlap that of either of the other African pongids. Little is known of the natural history of the pygmy chimpanzee beyond the fact that it is a forest animal, and it will not figure again in this book.

The gorilla falls into three major groups: the large population inhabiting the lowland forest of the Cameroons and western part of the Congo basin; the much smaller population in a similar habitat in the extreme east of the Congo Republic; and the tiny population of the highlands on the eastern border of the Congo and extreme west of Uganda. Of these, only the last, the mountain gorilla, has been extensively studied in the wild, but the essential features of gorilla natural history are probably similar throughout the three regions.

Structurally, gorillas are tree-climbers, or even brachiators. The mountain gorillas that have been observed in the wild, however, seldom climbed trees and never brachiated, presumably because their bulk (an adult male can weigh over four hundred pounds and is by far the heaviest of the primates now extant) had outgrown the trees available in mountain forest. In the lowland forests where larger trees are found the gorillas may well be more arboreal. Gorillas feed upon bulky vegetable foods which have a high proportion of roughage, such as bamboos and other shrubs, vines and foliage.

The chimpanzee is the most adaptable of the living great apes.

45

Probably for this reason it is the least threatened by human pressure, although the demands of zoos and medical research have almost exterminated it from parts of its range. The latter extends across the whole width of the tropical forest belt of Africa, from Liberia to Uganda and south into northern Tanzania. At the rain forest boundaries the chimp ranges into wooded savannah. The chimp is essentially an arboreal animal, and in the forests which are its typical habitat spends most of its time in the trees, feeding upon fruits and tender foliage. It uses tracks on the forest floor to travel from one feeding tree to another, however, and in more open country it may spend a good deal of its time on the ground. When in the trees the chimp progresses quadrupedally along branches, when these are stout enough, or swings and clambers beneath them. On the ground its gait is usually quadrupedal, with the knuckles taking the weight of the forepart of the body, but bipedal walking over short distances has often been observed, as indeed it has in many Cerco-pithecoid monkeys also.

The orang-utan (*Pongo pygmaeus*) is confined to the islands of Sumatra and Borneo. These two populations are relics of a much wider distribution which, in the Pleistocene period, extended into southern China. They are desperately threatened by human encroachment by farmers and hunters, and are close to extinction.

The orang is a large animal, second only to the gorilla in size. Its loose, shaggy red-brown hair is strikingly different from the black pelage of the African pongids. The shape of the skull, hands and feet is also rather different in the orang. Another peculiarity is the development in the adult male of broad, leathery-looking flaps along the sides of the face. The function of these is unknown.

The orang feeds almost exclusively upon forest fruits. It is the most arboreal of the living Pongidae. Its arms are long and frequently used in brachiation, but its more usual mode of progression is a leisurely 'quadrumanous' climbing, in which the legs and feet are almost as mobile as the arms and hands. Very little is known about the social behaviour of wild orangs. In all probability this has already been irretrievably modified by human persecution and gross population reduction.

This must conclude our brief sketch of the Order Primates as it is represented among extant faunas. The most striking fact about our knowledge of the group as a whole, particularly the natural history and social organization of its members, is its incompleteness. Some genera of the Cercopithecidae have been fairly adequately covered. In the remaining families there are wide gaps still to be filled, and we can be sure that these will produce some surprises. The reader must therefore judge for himself the value of any generalizations (even those made in this book!) which claim validity over the whole field of primate behaviour.

CHAPTER THREE

Behavioural Studies

INTRODUCTION: THE TASK

Looking back over the exploits of the pioneers of the studies we are about to examine, one feels awed at the imaginative insight which not only sent these explorers to far distant parts of the world, but prompted them to open up a completely new world, one which in his earlier travels man had not only overlooked but done much to destroy.

Interference with wild species on the scale practised in modern times has resulted in the reduction or confinement, sometimes both, of various species by man. This has come about directly by the extension of agriculture, a process which simultaneously alters the habitat and the availability of food and may bring about increase or decrease in numbers, and indirectly by the introduction of predators, against which indigenous animal populations have no prepared defences. Again, sometimes specific predators are eliminated. Often we are unaware of our relation to animals in their wild state, since we cannot assess how far our influence extends beyond what we can see. It is likely that wild animals will always be influenced by man, going by the effects of previous contact, so it is important that we should be able to define the extent and nature of the relationship.

The observers who are responsible for the varied investigations reported in this chapter adopted their particular methods of observation in the belief that they minimized the interference of the observers' presence. It will be seen, however, that to some extent their presence was felt by their subjects, and to understand fully what they saw, and the new material which they unearthed we must reassess the relationship between observer and the observed. Social anthropologists, who explicitly accept this in their relationship with communities under investigation, could well assist in redefining the position.

It is instructive to note what difficulties these early observers encountered, and what methods they used to overcome them. Carpenter and Washburn in their initial study of the gibbon in Siam opted to study a population in the neighbourhood of Buddhist temples. They also utilized forest cuttings as well as tall trees and cliff faces to observe the tree-top population. Southwick found that the topography of a Hindu temple in India inhabited by rhesus monkeys provided unique advantages; the bonnet macaque was studied between villages and along the roads of the same area by Simonds. All these populations were well acquainted with man.

The Japanese used provisioning to get a view of the communities of Japanese macaques in enclosed peninsulas of their natural habitat, and the same process was used by Goodall to close the remaining distance between herself and the chimpanzees of the Gombe Reserve, after familiarity with her presence had reduced the distance between them to thirty feet. She has been rightly praised for her patience and perseverance in allowing the apes to become fully familiar with her, as it enabled her to uncover much new material. But what un- suspected influence she may have had (similar to that, perhaps, of Phyllis Jay, who familiarized herself with the elementary repertoires of the langur and used them as a means of being accepted within the troop itself) has not been mooted, let alone assessed.

Hall's experience with baboons in the Cape Province convinced him that his presence was always affecting the young 'sentinel' baboons, and DeVore chose to make his observations from a Jeep when he was studying baboons in Nairobi National Park. Kortlandt concealed himself in a hide in order to study groups of chimpanzees, and the Reynolds observed chimpanzees by stealing up on them.

Each field worker is his own planner, manager, supplier, observer and recorder, and is lucky if he has an assistant for part or whole of the time he is in the field. Since the diversity of approach reflects differences of awareness and interpretation, there would be theoretical as well as practical advantages to mounting a joint expedition to make an intensive study of a few carefully selected species.

D

THE MACAQUES

Rhesus monkey (Plate 1)

The rhesus monkey (*Macaca mulatta*), the most ubiquitous laboratory primate, had long been used for physiological and medical studies before anything was known about its behaviour.

In 1942 Carpenter[1] was the first to study the behaviour of a colony of captured rhesus monkeys, liberated on Cayo Santiago Island in the Caribbean. Then in 1956 Chance[2] made an intensive study of similarly captive macaques, kept in an enclosure at the London Zoo. Only recently, however, have studies been made of the indigenous populations of northern India. There the rhesus monkeys are distributed from Kashmir and Gujarat (north of Bombay) in the west to the northern coast of the Bay of Bengal in the east. Their northern limit lies along the lower slopes of the Himalayas, where they live up to the snow-line. The seasonal temperature in their natural habitat fluctuates between 2 and 10 degrees Centigrade at night and 15 to 27 degrees Centigrade in the daytime. The rainfall is considerable.

Nowhere in the world is there such density of human habitation as in the river valleys of northern India and Pakistan. It is therefore not surprising that the largest single ecological factor in the lives of this species is their relationship to man. Man has not only changed the nature of the vegetation from forest to cultivated land, but he also provides special habitats or 'refuges' for the rhesus monkeys in villages or towns where they are either regarded as partially protected animals or kept for entertainment.

Rhesus monkeys of today have taken advantage of an ecological niche provided by man in which food is plentiful, and it seems likely that they have done so for the past five thousand years. We are observing here the behaviour of the macaque in an extremely dense population of monkeys in which an abundant food supply has been created by man. In this particular study material will be drawn from both the 'wild' population and from those other studies which have been made in semi-captive conditions where, perhaps, the behaviour represents (as far as the composition of the colony permits) the type of behaviour seen in the urban and temple areas of the wild population.

In the late 'fifties, Southwick, Beg and Siddiqi[3] carried out a survey in Uttar Pradesh, which forms the centre of the monkey's range. The area has a human population of 73 million with a density of 650 per square mile, 86 per cent of the population being rural. Approximately 65 per cent of the area produces such crops as various cereals, ground nuts, potatoes and cotton; 21 per cent is divided between the towns and villages and only 14 per cent remains forest, largely in the foothills and mountains.

The distribution of the monkey population is: 46 per cent in and around villages, 30 per cent in cities and towns, 12 per cent in forests and the remainder (in declining order of importance) on roadsides, canal banks, in temples and railroad stations. Most rhesus monkeys grow up familiar with man as part of their natural environment, so transporting animals from the wild to semi-captive conditions constitutes less of a change for them than it would for other species.

Southwick and his colleagues chose to study the groups which live in the neighbourhood of Hindu temples because:

1. The monkeys in the temple grounds are fed and partially protected by the local people, so that they are tame and easy to observe.
2. The temple grounds are larger and the monkeys are more completely represented at all ages than groups in most other habitats.
3. They appear to have the same age and class structures as the forest-dwelling macaques.

Method of observation
Temple macaques were observed in two ways:

1. From a vantage point which gave a commanding view of the central area.
2. On other occasions troops were followed around as they moved from their sleeping location to the area of most activity during daytime. A typical day would then afford five hours of observation, restricted to the active periods in the early morning and late afternoon. As a consequence of the interest taken by the local people in the observers and their modern equipment, the methods of observation had to be restricted.

The rhesus population of the whole area was found in about 20 groups, each numbering between 14 and 20 individuals. In this population adult females outnumbered adult males by 2 to 1; there were 4 males, 8 adult females, 5 infants and 1 or 2 sub-adults in the average group.

The observation area was a temple precinct surrounding an artificial lake. The temple population added up to approximately 100 rhesus monkeys in all, and was divided into 4 groups. In the groups inhabiting the temples, on average the adult females outnumbered adult males in the ratio of approximately 1·4 to 1. Juveniles appeared to outnumber infants rather more than in the population as a whole.

When the study started there were actually three groups. One of these soon split and the fourth set up its territory on the left of the artificial lake in the north-west temple. Group size and composition varied daily. Group 1, for example, varied between 37 and 44, and similar variations took place in other groups. This was in part due to the exchange of individuals between groups. Juveniles, in particular, spent several hours at a time with juveniles of another group. Females also occasionally crossed over for brief periods. Twice, adult males were seen to change groups temporarily. Adult males of subordinate rank left their groups for periods of time, often several hours, and could be absent from the area for hours or days at a time. Three peripheral males which normally maintained a solitary existence would occasionally enter the fringe of either group 1 or 2. Permanent changes also took place; these were caused by the death of adults or the birth of young, and also because local shopkeepers in the north bazaar area trapped some of the juveniles.

Southwick distinguished sub-groups within each group by noting their spatial separation. A sub-group was defined as a social segregation within a group which was more stable than a temporary association of individuals engaged in mutual grooming, juvenile play or sexual consort relations. These types of association occurred primarily, but not exclusively, between members of a sub-group. In group 1 there were three sub-groups; the first, central, sub-group consisting of 2 dominant males, 1 sub-dominant male and an aggregation of approximately 8 females, 2 infants and 8 juveniles. Because of its central position this sub-group formed the core of group 1. The activity of its members largely determined the pattern of movement and daily routine of the group. The second, or 'peripheral', sub-group consisted of 1 very aggressive, highly dominant male and 4 females, 2 infants and 7 juveniles. The third sub-group was composed of 5 young adult males of subordinate social rank. The use of subordinate in this context refers to the relationship of the different sub-groups, especially in so far as they are distinguished by the initiative taken in directing the whole group's activities and, as a consequence, the way each sub-group behaved during the daily routine. The initiative was often taken by juveniles and females, who were the first to be active, but a definite progression from one part of the area to another did not take place until one or other of the males of the central sub-group participated. Thus one may conclude that it is the awareness of these central sub-group males which ultimately gave direction to the movement of the whole of group 1.

Ten to fifteen minutes later the 'peripheral' sub-group would follow, a hundred to two hundred yards behind. At some moment after the core sub-group had begun its progression, the males of the subordinate groups would start to fan out into the neighbouring areas, where they would make direct contact with other groups and be responsible for the aggressive encounters arising between groups.

The social organization of group 2 consisted of only two sub-groups. The main sub-group consisted of 3 adult males, 10 adult females, 8 infants and 9 juveniles. The subordinate sub-group of group 2 consisted of the males which ranged the periphery of the central group and were, like their counterparts in group 1, particularly active in group movement and aggressive encounters between this group and others. Isolated peripheral males moved into both of the subordinate male sub-groups of group 1 and group 2.

The Japanese macaque (Plate 2)

This species inhabits the southern island of Japan where it is under continuous study by the workers of Kyoto University.

Group structure

The group structure is very similar to that of the rhesus, but the group is considerably larger, consisting of some 200 individuals (see

Figure 2, page 55). The subordinate maturing males form a peripheral group surrounding a central heterosexual group, and adult males living alone associate with this subordinate male periphery at times.

In an open space the monkeys are regularly provided with potatoes, and the structure of their society becomes apparent from the spatial arrangement at the provisioning site and as the group leaves it.

Russell and Russell[4] maintain that provisioning is not only responsible for the large size of the groups but also distorts the social structure.

The following quotations from Itani's description[5] of the departure of the group from the feeding area illustrate the stability of some parts of the group and the relative amounts of interchange that take place between others. (The dominant males are the first to leave.)

> The sub-dominant males which were on the periphery of the feeding ground now enter the group of females and children left after the dominant males have gone, but do so only after the last of these has left ...
>
> We now have a group whose centre is formed by the sub-dominant males; the pattern is less stable than before. There are still some sub-dominant males of a lower rank that cannot enter the feeding place, and one animal often tries to drive the others away.

Soon, however, the females and young start retiring to the forest, usually in groups of two or three. They leave behind two- or three-year-old sub-dominant males, often with one or two females. But when the subadult males that are still standing on the edge of the feeding ground enter it they drive away the females that are left. The sub-dominant males that occupy the centre of the group may show a complete lack of interest or may even co-operate with the subadult males in driving away the remaining females. So we have a new grouping pattern, comprising only males. This group consists of the sub-dominant males, the subadult males and any juvenile males (two or three years old) that are still left. At this moment there is no longer any animal waiting outside the feeding place to enter it. This type of grouping is temporary. The main body of the group is moving towards the woods, and as the place where they go is not very far away the continuity of the group is never interrupted. Finally, grasping potatoes in their hands, the remaining males move off into the forest, keeping clear of each other.

From this description it can clearly be seen that the adult dominant males form a central separate group, with which all females and

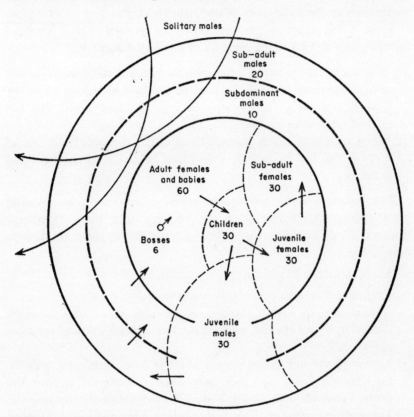

FIGURE 2: Spatial organization of Japanese macaques, *Macaca fuscata*, of Takasakiyama (*from Itani*). Note: (1) movement of solitary males, through fringe of troop, (2) movement of young animals during maturation

young associate, and that the sub-groups of sub-dominant males and subadult males (with a less stable relationship between each other) both keep their distance from this central heterosexual group. Juvenile males, on the other hand, appear to be able to wander at random to and fro across this boundary. Although there is evidence of repulsion between the sub-dominant and subadult males and the dominant males of the central sub-group, the community as a whole keeps together.

Agonistic relations

An agonistic state exists where there is a conflict between two tendencies in the behaviour of the individual.

Rank order relations between males are assessed by the Japanese by reference to two characteristics of dominant animals:

1. When a potato is thrown between two males, the dominant will take it wherever it comes to rest; on the rare occasions when the subordinate takes the potato, he will be chased with his tail curved back over his body.
2. When a monkey finds himself temporarily the dominant one of a cluster he has entered, he raises and holds his tail straight and vertical.

The Japanese workers mention, among other criteria for assessing rank order, withdrawal from the vicinity of a more dominant animal. Then, in decreasing order of importance, subordinate acts consist of:

1. Leaving food for more dominant monkeys.
2. Redirected attacks on neighbouring monkeys.
3. Assumption of facial expressions of 'defence'. (This involves flickering of the eyelids, uncovering the upper teeth and opening the mouth very wide.)
4. Lowering the tail in the presence of the more dominant animal.
5. Finally, the body and face may also be flattened against the ground and the axis of the body directed obliquely towards the approaching monkey. This position is maintained and is ignored by the dominant, so enabling the submissive monkey to remain where it is.

The last is the definition of a 'submissive posture'.

It is characteristic of the attacks of a dominant male that they are both simple and intense. By this is meant that there is little hesitation in the way it approaches and ultimately bites its opponent, but once the biting has been done the male pays no more attention to the animal, particularly if it is female. Most of the attacks *are* on females, by virtue of the organization of the group, since the females are always in the vicinity of the dominant males. As soon as the bite has been given the male walks back among the group with his tail vertical and straight. Other attacks are directed against the sub-dominant males and subadult males which transgress the central area. Itani's classification of attacks made by dominant animals on others is unsatisfactory because it combines categories which are a description of the type of attack (defined by the direction and type of individual towards which it is directed) with others that are included in the list on the basis of their outcome. As a result they will not here be treated in these categories. By giving instances of each kind of attack it will be possible to redefine them as follows:

1. An 'emotional' type of attack. This occurred most frequently between dominant and sub-dominant males and between dominant males and the females. It appeared only when food was taken by the subordinate animals in the neighbourhood of the dominant one. The larger the social distance between them, the more frequent the attack. Since the subordinate had not judged his opportunities very well, it usually led to a chase. As it did not occur very much among the most dominant males, it looks as if the transgression of some social space was an important factor in precipitating the attack.

2. This category is concerned with dominant animals attacking one of a number that are already involved in agonistic encounters with other animals. This type of attack is classified by Itani as 'intended to restore order; controlling or suppressing a disturbance', but the examples given are of what Kummer calls 'protected threat' (see Figure 5, page 73). For example, after two females had been threatening each other, the weaker of the two went towards her more dominant ♀ partner. The other examples suggest that the occurrence of aggressive behaviour in the neighbourhood of a dominant animal might be the precipitating factor.

3. The third category involves subordinate monkeys joining in an attack, as when the overlord male started attacking a female that had taken food from in front of him and immediately three of the other members of the dominant hierarchy joined in the threats or attacks and enabled the overlord to catch the female and bite her neck. She finally ran away and the males did not follow, but barked after her. However, as she ran through the subadult male section

they took up the chase. This looks like an extended form of protected threat. Russell and Russell call this 'band-wagon'.

It appears that a young monkey can be attacked by dominant males when it has left the neighbourhood of a female even if that female is grooming the dominant animal at the time, but the attackers are made to desist by the screeching of the female. Attacks by the dominant males are also made against (1) individuals that attempt to penetrate into the central part of the group, (2) females in oestrus and (3) non-members of the group.

Itani also describes how the subadult males attack solitary males which come in individually to make contact with the females. While these solitary males are not deterred by the threats and attacks of individual subadult males, they are sometimes put off if these combine together, and they can eventually be chased away, especially if a sub-dominant male joins in.

Now let us look again at the rhesus monkeys studied by Southwick[6] in the Indian temples and discuss the types of group organization encountered there in the light of these definitions of aggression. In the central male sub-group of group 1 two elderly males were dominant over the one sub-dominant male. They were usually relaxed and closely associated and rarely did aggressive encounters occur between them, nor did they compete for food. The dominant male of the peripheral male sub-group was very much more aggressive and, whenever he happened to come across one of the dominant males of the central sub-group he would be dominant over either alone. As they usually kept together, however, he would retreat in face of their combined opposition. Despite the incidence of agonistic behaviour between these males, they would unite co-operatively in group attacks against other groups. The separation of the two sub-groups in this instance helped considerably to keep these males apart. In the central sub-group of group 2 one male dominated the other two.

Itani states that the relationships between males of the adult hierarchies varied from very relaxed to highly aggressive agonistic encounters.

In both the Japanese macaque group and the group of Indian rhesus monkeys of the temples, the relationships between the monkeys low down in the hierarchy were much less stable than those between animals of a higher rank order. This was manifest in two ways:

1. Those low in the hierarchy became involved in a much greater number of agonistic encounters. (This was also characteristic of the monkeys of the breeding hierarchy in the zoo colony studied by Chance.)

2. Whereas animals high in rank remained in stable relationship to one another, those at the bottom of the hierarchy could occasionally be seen to change their relative status, including male/female relationships.

Sexual relations

Surveys of a number of different European and tropical zoos reveal that there is a birth peak for rhesus monkeys at one time in the year, which is characteristic of, and different for each colony. Correspondingly, some four to five months before that, there is an increase in sexual behaviour, made evident not only by the number of copulations but also by the number and intensity of agonistic encounters, especially among the adult males. It appears that there is the same periodicity of sexual behaviour in the rhesus monkeys of the Indian temple communities, the peak there being around September.

As has been observed in captive colonies, females form consort relations with males of the hierarchy lasting from a few hours to several days. During this period several bouts of copulation take place, only some of which appear to be accompanied by ejaculations. When this occurs both partners bare their teeth, the male emitting a high-pitched staccato note, and the female frequently turns its head sideways towards the male as if attempting to see it, often reaching back towards the male with its foreleg. During the establishment of the consort relationship males attack the active soliciting females. Studies of the captive colony at the London Zoo showed that this was because in this particular colony the females coming into oestrus solicited by threatening their prospective overlords and, unless this behaviour was combined with a suitable degree of submission, their threatening behaviour provoked retaliatory attacks which could be sufficiently severe to wound and deter them from further courtship. In the Bristol colony the females solicited by lipsmacking gestures and were less subject to attack as a result.

59

(Lipsmacking is described as a rapid opening or closing of the lips, while the ears are flattened against the head.) This appears to be a 'cultural' difference between the colonies of the London and Bristol zoos.[7]

Once their consortship is established, the partners move about together and frequently groom one another. But the grooming of females by adult males was practically confined to this period, probably because after the consort relationship has broken up the females return to groups of other females, sometimes to a special individual with which they spend most of the time and have a very persistent bond. Aggressive behaviour between females appeared to increase just before the onset of oestrus periods and after that to decline. In group 1 of the wild rhesus the females moved readily across the boundary between the central and peripheral male sub-groups.

The bonnet macaque (Plate 3)

Paul Simonds[8] made an interesting study of the bonnet macaque (*Macaca radiata*), the common macaque of part of the Indian sub-continent. The bonnet macaque is a slender, long-tailed monkey, with pronounced sex dimorphism, grey-brown hair on the back and a white or grey belly. Its facial skin is light pink or red, and the hair on the head is parted in the centre to give it the 'bonnet'.

Habitat

The bonnet macaque is found in a very wide variety of habitats ranging from semi-desert to rain forests, but two major ecological niches are occupied:

1. a variety of forests;
2. areas of human cultivation, habitats in which the langur and rhesus monkeys are also found.

Simonds made an extensive study on a group with a home range entirely within a cultivated area. There the macaques lived for preference in the neighbourhood of tall, spreading fig (banyan) trees, from which they obtained both food and shelter. A third of their time was spent on the ground, the rest in these trees.

Group composition and relations between groups

The composition of two groups was recorded. In the first there were 18 adult and subadult males and 18 adult and subadult females. In the other there were 19 adult and subadult males and 11 adult and subadult females, the rest being juveniles and infants. It is not known to what extent this is a representative sample of population sex ratio, but it is noteworthy that in view of its sexual composition it is the only example so far known of a species of Anthropoidea in which a predominance of males has been found in the heterosexual group.

A typical range covered approximately two square miles, and the monkeys roamed out from the banyan trees in the core area over approximately one third of the range each day. Groups occasionally met in the overlapping regions of two ranges and the males would then sit staring at each other for some time before returning to their own range, followed by their own group. On all but one occasion it was the same group which retreated. On that occasion there was some screeching among the females of the usually dominant group, and the males of that group ran back into their own territory and were followed for some thirty yards by the males of the usually less dominant group. The group that was usually dominant then retreated further into its own core area and slept in different trees from usual, further removed from the neighbouring group.

Rank order and agonistic behaviour

If what is now reported about the bonnet macaque's social behaviour is carefully noted, it will become clearer that there is no way of comparing Simonds's observations with what has been said by Southwick and his collaborators about the rhesus monkey. In Simonds's study the salient features of the repertoire are noted, not only providing us with a clear understanding of how dominance status was assessed, but also enabling the observers themselves to assess this much more readily from a wider variety of clues. Moreover, comparison of the repertoire with that provided by Reynolds for the captive rhesus colony at the Whipsnade Zoo immediately reveals that the two species of macaque have social repertoires of different structures.

Simonds places the preferential access of one monkey rather than another to food which has been thrown between them in the fore-front of his criteria for assessing rank order, but makes it plain that a subordinate monkey will always give way on the approach of a dominant monkey or make one of several subordination gestures instead of retiring. For example, looking away from the domin-ant animal may be a substitute for actually moving away, or the subordinate monkey may lipsmack or present to the dominant monkey.

Having assessed the relative status of a monkey on the basis of whether or not it moves away from another, and having seen that various submissive gestures can replace movement away, Simonds was then able to note behaviour which was restricted to dominant animals in an encounter. The sniffing of the face of one monkey by another is done only by dominant animals, as also is neck-chewing, which may be combined with embracing. When two males approach one another they may embrace, but only one will chew on the neck of the other. The combination of embracing and neck-chewing may end an encounter between a dominant and a submissive animal. The mounting of the subordinate by the dominant ends an encounter between rhesus monkeys but not between bonnet macaques, as in this species the number of times the dominant animal mounts the subordinate and *vice versa* are approximately equal. This may be partly due to the fact that the dominant monkey sometimes solicits mounting by a subordinate one, and although the subordinate may try to avoid this he is frequently forced into the position where he must and does in fact mount. Clearly, a full understanding of the bonnet macaques' social repertoire as compared with that of other species must await sequence analysis (see Chapter 6).

Slapping, stare-threatening, eyelid threatening, open-mouth threatening, growl-threatening were all given the same low-level aggressive connotation by Simonds, as judged by the effect on the spatial separation of monkeys. These various gestures were used to rank the males of a group. There then appeared a central rank order of five dominant males distinguished from the others by their active interaction with other sections of the group. For example, they moved towards and broke up agonistic encounters of other members, acted as a focus of the group (the females and infants remaining in their vicinity) and they determined the direction of the group movement. They were not threatened by males of the other parts of the group.

Four other adult males were subordinate to the central males and behaved somewhat differently. They were spatially separated and tended to avoid threat situations wherever they arose. They were often threatened by monkeys they approached, rather than being the instigators of threats. The threat would then be displaced on to another animal by the animals which they approached. The central males were larger and more muscular and had excellent canines, whereas without exception less dominant males had smaller or broken canines. The males of the central rank order did not combine together in support of each other in threat, whereas the others did.

Finally, there was a very old canineless male which was subordinate to the central males and not very-active socially in threat sequences and other agonistic behaviour; but his presence had the same effect as the central males' in that it suppressed fighting in his neighbourhood, and he was never threatened. There were no isolated males living outside the group. The various types of males could move readily through the area of more dominant males, provided they gave suitable submission gestures.

On the basis of this study the bonnet macaque appears to show the same essential differentiation amongst adult males as is shown by other macaques.

Although deaths due to wounding are not common in this species a major fight between the cohort males (in which the alpha male was deposed) resulted in all the males being wounded, some very badly. Slashes as long as four inches and deep punctures were inflicted on each other on head, hips and shoulders. Three months later they had all healed. This process of healing appeared to be assisted by one monkey grooming another and thereby cleaning the wounds. A wounded monkey would present itself for grooming and receive it from a number of different animals, gaining attention apparently in proportion to the severity of the wound. It is interesting in view of the lack of information about the cleaning function of grooming in other species that animals grooming wounded bonnet macaques have been seen to pick dirt out of the wound and then lick it clean.

Play

Another feature of the bonnet macaque is that the males play with monkeys of all ages from about six months old to fully adult males, whereas the rhesus monkey adults never play, either with each other or with young monkeys. Wrestling and grappling are the main types of play behaviour, but both species will sometimes learn to swim and play in the water. Unlike the rhesus, the bonnet macaque during play does not use strong threat gestures or show signs of attack, and there is no biting or breaking the skin, no growling, screeching or lunging. These normally occur in threat sequences in subhuman primate social repertoire.

In the bonnet macaque the difference between the play of adults and young is that chase-play is primarily an infant play. Low growling and eyelid threats might enter into the play of the young, but subadults and adult males do not behave like this. There is a great variation in the amount of play shown by different individuals. Play behaviour was solicited by a bouncy walk, with the head twisted to one side. Altmann described an invitation to play by rhesus monkeys where the monkey places its head between its fore and hind legs and looks backwards at a likely playfellow.

Relations between the sexes

Very clear-cut and significant differences exist between the sexual behaviour of the bonnet macaque and the rhesus monkey. The bonnet macaque forms no consort relationship like that of the rhesus, in which a female will attend a dominant male during the peak of oestrus and no other monkey may mate with the female while the relationship exists. A bonnet macaque female, having mated with a high-ranking male, may immediately mate with others in the society and then again with the same dominant male, who does not in any way attempt to interfere with these other relationships. The male bonnet macaque does the majority of the soliciting. There is no pronounced sexual skin, and there is very little change in colour of the red skin at different periods in the cycle. Finally, copulations are always achieved from a single mounting and a single series of pelvic thrusts. This pattern is clear-cut in the group studied by Simonds but this type of relationship may vary intra-specifically (see Chapter 7).

Grooming in macaque societies

Probably more grooming is done in a bonnet macaque society than among the rhesus and Japanese macaques and possibly even than in baboon societies. More individuals take an active part in the grooming among the bonnet macaques, and the grooming activities are less restricted within categories than in the rhesus macaque society studied by Reynolds at the Whipsnade Zoo. In fact, the bonnet macaque grooms partners at random.

In the absence of any statement by Southwick and his colleagues about the pattern of grooming activity of the rhesus monkey in North India we must fall back on the evidence provided by Reynolds in his study at Whipsnade. Reynolds found that the rhesus monkeys of this colony did not direct grooming at random, like the bonnet macaques, but at specific partners, so that in certain cases we may justifiably speak of grooming partners and grooming partnerships. These partnerships may be exclusive for a given period, or an animal may have more than one grooming partner at the same time. In certain instances, the grooming partnerships consist of a one-way relationship only, in which one animal does most or all of the grooming. In other grooming partnerships both animals groom each other an equal and large amount. Although throughout the colony as a whole there is a correlation of grooming with status, individual instances occur in which the reciprocal grooming, or one-way grooming, is not related to status. Reynolds found only three instances of grooming relationships of a very persistent character where one or both concerned were outside the adult rank order (especially where one-year-old monkeys were involved), and he suggests that this is because grooming can express itself where it is not in conflict with a withdrawal tendency produced by adult rank order relations. The majority of grooming partnerships between adult males and adult females may swing from being predominantly male-grooming-female to predominantly female-grooming-male, and are at other times reciprocal. Males, on the whole, groom less than females, but both sexes do an increasing amount of grooming as they grow older, and in adult males the amount they do is positively correlated with position in the male hierarchy. The lowest-ranking male may not groom at all. In adult females, a very different situation

E

65

prevails; those females which are not in the mating hierarchy groom most.

In those features of grooming behaviour reported by Itani the Japanese macaque differs markedly from the rhesus monkey. For example, reciprocity of grooming is certain in any of the Japanese macaque relationships, even if it is the dominant male who grooms a youngster of two years old. The exceptions seem to have social importance. The first is when a mother grooms her youngster: this is a unilateral process – the baby has not yet learnt how to groom – and this was the same for the mother grooming the young rhesus. The second is when adult male Japanese macaques groom the one-year-old youngsters at the time when their mothers are giving birth to the next infant.

In the Japanese macaque an interesting example of a form of soliciting for grooming is displayed when a more dominant male goes in front of a less dominant one and shows him his tail. This is followed by the less dominant one mounting the dominant, a gesture also found in bonnet macaques and langurs. When it is over, in the Japanese macaque, the subordinate starts grooming the one who had initially presented himself with raised tail.

THE BABOONS

Savannah baboons (Plates 4 and 5)

Hall and DeVore[9] studied the chacma baboon in the Cape Nature Reserve, Cape Province, and in the Drakensberg Mountains of the southern Cape Province, and DeVore and Washburn[10] studied the yellow baboon of the Amboseli Reserve in Kenya and the olive baboon of the Nairobi National Park – areas chosen for the open nature of the terrain and the good visibility.

It was only possible to study the baboons' social behaviour with minimum interference by allowing them to become used to the presence of the observers. But the various methods of observing the groups may have had an undue influence on what they found.

The most revealing results come from Nairobi. The groups were followed throughout the day and observed from a Land Rover carrying a wide range of equipment. Sometimes it was possible to assess the numbers and composition of a group two hundred yards away by using binoculars, but the details of the behaviour could be studied only from a distance of less than twenty-five yards. Occasionally a group's size and components were checked as its members crossed a path or (in Cape Province) from blinds which were constructed opposite sleeping cliffs.

Groups varied in size within any one area. In all areas the smallest contained about 10 members. The mean size of the groups in the Amboseli park was 80 (where the largest contained 185), twice as large as that in the Nairobi National Park. In the Drakensberg Mountains the higher the altitude, the smaller the mean size. There is less food at high altitudes, and these facts may be related. The fact that a group of 12 and another of 185 share the same area, however, suggests that the pattern of social behaviour *within* the group, rather than the nature of the terrain, is responsible for the size of the group.

One group in the Amboseli Park consisted of 2 sub-groups with 66 and 37 individuals respectively, and these often separated and re-joined during the day's movements and slept adjacent to each other. This type of association, and also the coming together at points of mutual interest such as water-holes, made assessment of group composition difficult without repeated contact and familiarity.

Where baboons are regarded as pests, shooting by man alters the composition of the groups; therefore groups from such areas have been omitted from the following estimate. The proportion of adult females to adult males has been reported to be between 3 and 5 to 1, but careful assessment of this ratio in 6 groups from protected areas revealed that a total female/male count may be deceptive, because of the different rate of maturation for males and females. Females reach mating age between three and a half and four years and carry their first young by the age of five, whereas males, though sexually mature by five, take from seven to ten years to attain full physical growth, i.e. full eruption of canine teeth, muscular and skeletal maturity and the growth of the shoulder mantle.

All adult females with young will appear adult, but the males will not be taken to be adult until they are twice as old. So, whereas the adult sex ratio shows the typical bias in favour of the females reported to some extent for most social monkeys, in the savannah baboon there appears to be no real evidence for this. It is probably significant that no excluded males exist, either alone or as bachelor bands.

Plant food of many types, including flowers, seeds, bulbs, bases of leaves and stems and fruit, forms the staple diet of baboons. Grasses were eaten daily during the period of observation in Kenya, different parts being eaten according to season. A most noticeable aspect of feeding behaviour is the diversity of food selected; the most typical feeding behaviour is the habit of exploring close to, or just under, the surface of the ground, where the baboons dig for tubers with high water content (passed over by ungulates) in the dry season. The insects they find by turning over stones can become at times a major part of the diet, which includes scorpions, centipedes and the legless lizard. On the same sea coast of Cape Province the baboons catch crabs, sand-hoppers and shell-fish; limpets are pulled off and cracked open with the back molars. Baboons have been seen to catch and eat a hare which had 'frozen' after being chased. Young gazelles and young plovers were taken when suddenly discovered. It should be noted that many of the above activities require strong muscular effort. No systematic search for any of these prey was seen, however, and one baboon was seen to catch a vervet monkey and release it unharmed. DeVore points out that the assertion that hardship and drought force the baboons to kill lambs is not borne out by these observations, as the gazelles referred to earlier were caught and eaten in the rainy season, when vegetable matter was plentiful.

The baboons' feeding habits appear to be dominated by a tendency to pay attention to the surface of the ground for signs of what may be just below the surface. Tame baboons, liberated into a group, were found searching in the exact spot where neighbouring animals had just finished scraping the soil away. Learning by observation and imitation of the other members of the group would therefore appear to be important in establishing the location, if not the mode, of feeding adopted by the whole group, and is a significant contribution to the adaptability of their feeding habits.

It is important to realize that baboons are semi-terrestrial animals and that though they take refuge where possible they are also adapted to meet predators in open country.

Baboons live in closed groups and seem to sleep in the safest places available; that is usually in trees or on cliff ledges, though sometimes they occupy a cave. The number and nature of such sites depends on what is available within the core area of their home range. This core is the region within which they are most frequently found, though they may go outside it during the daily forage for food. The average daily distance travelled is about three miles,

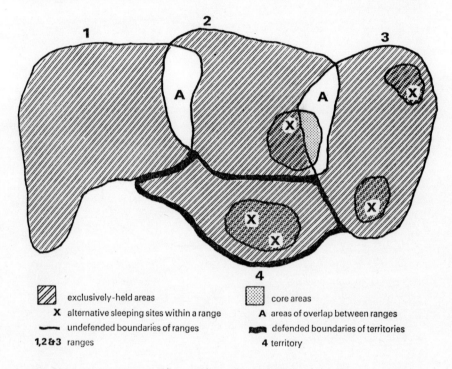

FIGURE 3: Types of living space and their components

traced in a direct line along the route, but individuals traverse much more country in the course of their meanderings. Occasionally the group shifts to a new core area within the home range. Core areas and the extent of overlap between home ranges are indicated in Figures 3 and 4. Contact between neighbouring groups is less than might be expected from the extent of overlap because groups avoid one another, but it is made easier if there is more than one core area in a home range. At most times groups which meet regularly do so without hostility. As many as five hundred baboons from a number of groups may congregate at a water-hole, but when some groups meet, clusters of males within each group gather at points where the groups are adjacent to one another and gestures and vocalizing may accompany the gradual displacement of a smaller group by a large one. Fighting between groups trying to settle in the same sleeping tree has been observed.

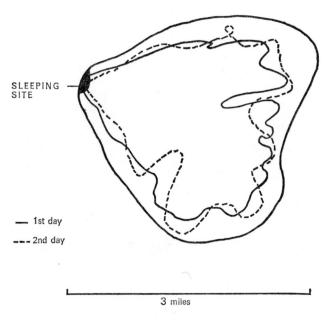

SLEEPING SITE

—— 1st day

--- 2nd day

3 miles

FIGURE 4: Typical daily excursions within a range from a single sleeping site of savannah baboons. (*After DeVore and Hall*)

When, in their search for food, baboons move away from the shelter of trees and cliffs into the open savannah, they are exposed to predators in a way in which no arboreal or forest-dwelling primates are. The predators include lions, leopards, cheetahs, hyenas, jackals, wild dogs and raptorial birds. No direct attack has been reported, except by a hyena on an isolated male. Baboons react defensively when encountering a likely predator by taking refuge in trees or making a detour. In parts of the Amboseli Reserve where trees to serve as refuges are absent and lions numerous, baboons may be denied access to rich food sources. Thus awareness of predators or the need to take refuge during periods of rest necessarily circum-scribe their range of activity.

The savannah of Africa provides a gradation of ecological features. At one end, parts bordering the forests provide large trees, singly and in clumps, interspersed with grass and scrub, and at the other the grasslands are sparsely dotted with scrub and small trees. The open undulating plain (with some trees, but little grass) is inter-spersed with occasional crags and outcrops of rock (which provide the centres of the core areas, and refuge), or else is mountainous, as in the Drakensberg of South Africa where cliff ledges provide shelter.

A noticeable feature of a baboon troop moving into open country is the order and arrangement of animals in the troop. The spatial arrangement while on the move is typical and constant and it can be seen as the best way of giving protection to the mothers with infants and of obtaining early warning of danger. Mothers carrying their infants tend to be found towards the middle of a group near the most dominant males; the less dominant males are to the front, at the sides and to the rear. Some subadult or young males would be ahead of the group by as much as two hundred yards.

Awareness of unusual events in the neighbourhood of the group may be communicated to the group as a whole (and particularly to the dominant males) by the barking of outlying subadult males, which come into contact with the disturbance first, by the barking of any member of the group, or through the vigilance of the domi-nant males. When this happens, the adult males move forward towards the disturbance. The defence of the group, when caught in the open, would appear to lie in the strength and aggressiveness of these adult males, whose large canines can be used as weapons of defence. Adult females, if left behind, maintain vigilance like adult males. Large males were seen to be vigilant before and after the group crossed roads. In open country the first reaction by members of the group to outside disturbance is to stop whatever they are doing and remain stationary, sometimes for hours, before making a detour, but when the dominant male is very actively moving about, stopping and scanning at intervals, the group closes round him.

Attack by predators and active defence against it by baboons has been observed; it can be seen that protection by large adult males would only occasionally have to be called upon to have survival value. Cohesion therefore enables the group to be defended against occasional and surprise attacks in open country. That cohesive behaviour of baboons is essentially defensive, and not an offensive form of group behaviour, can be seen from the prolonged waiting and detours to avoid danger and, when predators are around, the seeking out of the protection offered by trees.

The rank order of dominant males forms the centre around which the other members of the group are organized. In many groups there is one conspicuously dominant male, as was found in groups containing between 15 and 35 individuals, 1 of which was found in the Cape and 4 in Nairobi Park. A much more complex relationship, however, existed in one group of 28 animals, containing 6 adult males and 7 adult females.

> Although a stable and linear hierarchy sometimes exists, it is likely to represent only a temporary stage in the history of any one group, the pattern changing as younger males become fully grown and older males disappear. Equally impressive is the evidence of the possibility of shifts in dominance within neighbouring groups when an adult male changes from one group to another.[11]

Agonistic episodes took place between males of the central hierarchy (or rank order) in all groups, but much less frequently in the groups where one male was outstandingly dominant. These episodes could be triggered off by an attack by one of the members of a group upon another (as when an adult female attacked a female with an infant on her back), and in general were concentrated at the start and end of the day. The episodes consisted mainly of threat, counter-threat, rearrangement of the position of the animals and the chasing of one animal by another. During these episodes the rest of the group would keep well away from those involved. At other times the aggressiveness of the adult male, when directed at other members of the group (who have already gathered round him in response to disturbance outside the group) tends to reinforce the tendency to stay close to him. The dominant male was much more frequently involved in encounters within the group than any other male, except where the rank order relationships within a group were less stable or where two or more adult males constantly supported each other in encounters with others. Mothers with very young babies (identifiable as young because they were black) clustered near and walked close to the dominant males. These dominant males retaliated at attacks on these mothers.

The forms that agonistic behaviour takes in the savannah baboon have not been systematically studied; that is to say, no accurate description has been recorded of the postures and facial gestures together with the situations in which they occur and the reaction of the recipient. It is therefore not possible to give a satisfactory and objective assessment of the various types of 'threat'. Nevertheless, the forms appear similar to those of the macaque and hamadryas baboon; 'threat' being defined as a limited inhibited form of attack which falls short of biting. The most frequent form of agonistic situations involving threat were *redirection sequences*, in which one animal threatens another and the second then threatens a third. Both females and males were involved in this type of chain reaction. The choice of recipient of the redirected threat is as much circum-stantial as social. In the presence of a strange male baboon the dominant male of one group redirected his attacks on to many members within the group.

Protected threat

This is a triadic relation in which one baboon takes up a position so that the overlord is behind it. From this position of advantage it can solicit threats from the overlord on to a rival, thereby reinforcing its own threats and enhancing its own status. It was originally described by Kummer,[12] for the hamadryas (see Figure 5).

FIGURE 5: Protected threat. The centre monkey protected by his position in relation to the overlord male (*right*), threatens a monkey of superior status (*left*). (*From Kummer*)

73

Similarly, any male may solicit the supporting threat of a second towards its tormentor. When this is done by soliciting the threat of the overlord in support of its own aggression, the aggressor may be able to force a change in its own status in respect to the threatened baboon, which was initially dominant over it.

Other forms of agonistic behaviour

Two savannah baboon males dominated one group by mutually supporting threats. On another occasion two males simultaneously threatened one another. Yet another form of threat was called harassing. This occurred frequently in a group with a small number of females wherever one male formed a consort relationship with a female. Another male would move around the pair, accompanying this behaviour by yawning and audible tooth grinding, gradually closing in on the harassed pair. The harassing male eventually attacked, chased or bit the harassed male, the female being taken off by one of the males which may have joined in.

Agonistic episodes are therefore a characteristic feature of baboon groups. These involve complex agonistic relations between males of the society, at times drawing in females. The aggressiveness displayed within the group is at times clearly related to the aggressiveness of these males when aroused by outside events.

Rank order relations between females are much less dependent on overt threat and more on supplanting another female at a preferred site, such as a grooming partner. Dominance behaviour between females was observed, as when a dominant female, lowering the eyelids, stops in front of a subordinate. This causes the latter to move away.

All agonistic social behaviour which is not full aggression or recognizable escape appears to have a quality indicating ambivalent tendencies. What the nature of this ambivalence is cannot be known at present in the absence of a full understanding of the behaviour structure and of any adequate study of the functional outcomes.

An escaping female being chased by a dominant male typically runs screeching continuously with tail upright. If caught, or after escaping down a cliff in sight of a male, she crouches, crying with a long-drawn-out 'churring'. Her pursuer may also be arrested by her quickly halting and presenting to him. This is therefore a form of submission. Presenting, even in sexual behaviour, would always appear to be shown in an agonistic context, as it occurs in the behaviour of a subordinate or low-ranking animal when passing or being in the neighbourhood of a dominant animal.

Females not in oestrus present only briefly and scamper away. Adult females typically present to females with infants. Dominant adult males do likewise to near-by adult hierarchy males; in both latter instances the hindquarters are somewhat lowered. For some reason, DeVore and Hall do not classify all these forms as agonistic, although they take place in agonistic situations and are not typically sexual. A facial expression termed the 'fear grimace' appears to the observers to be closely related to escape and flight tendencies. In the baboon it is connected with the retraction of the lips without separating the teeth.

Mating in a social-context

Soliciting establishes a consort relationship and is a female activity, but when the consort relationship has been established either partner will initiate mating; to some extent this is dependent on differences between the partners and the stage of the consort relationship.

As females come into oestrus they cluster round the dominant male, but he takes no notice of them, even when they present. At this early stage of the cycle, however, less dominant males successfully mate with them without interference from the alpha (dominant) male. The dominant male mates with all the adult females during the peak of oestrus when their sexual skin is maximally swollen.

In groups with equal sex ratio between adults, harassment of the adult males frequently interferes with mating. In groups with unequal sex ratios where consort relations are formed, the consorts remain at a considerable distance from the group, reducing the likelihood of interference. It is not known to what extent, if at all, females at non-reproductive times of the cycle remain in the vicinity of males they have consorted with.

What ethologists call displacement activities occur only in conflict situations, and were observed and arbitrarily classified by DeVore and Hall as 'reactions denoting uncertainty' – yawning, shrugging of the shoulders, wiping the muzzle with the hand, scratching

75

shoulders and back, fiddling with food objects, frantic grooming of the partner while being harassed, and rapid copulation. Such out-of-context behaviour may arise in agitation or uncertainty from the activation of any behaviour system that happens to be or has recently been aroused, aided by the presence of relevant stimuli in the vicinity.

Grooming

All members of a group to some extent receive and give grooming attention, and this is a prominent sort of social behaviour, occurring most frequently early in the day, during the midday quiet period and when the group approaches its sleeping place at the end of the day. The amount of grooming attention an individual receives reflects his ranking in the dominance order, but within this general structure grooming takes place between females several times more frequently than between males. Adult males spend longer grooming oestrus females with whom they are in a temporary consort relationship than in any other situation. Females groom other females, especially when they are accompanied by young, and oestrus females are more frequently groomed than any other. Grooming is frequently initiated by the animal going up to and lying in front of another: this is typical of males towards females. Females go up to and present to males: the approached animal immediately starts to groom the initiator. Lipsmacking is frequent during grooming. Young animals frequently groom each other and infants are frequently groomed by their mothers or other females.

Greeting behaviour

Various types of behaviour occur on the approach of one animal to another. Lipsmacking is one, and it is often a prelude to many of the others. When strangers, as well as new infants, are accepted, a number of the following types of behaviour occur towards the 'stranger'. Standing on the hind legs near to him, raising the hind-quarters with one arm placed between the hind legs, putting the muzzle to the ano-genital region of the other animal or making mouth to mouth contact. These types of behaviour are frequent and are directed towards females with young infants. All this greeting behaviour takes place not when the animals are close to each other, but as one animal approaches another from a distance. The communicating animal briefly flattens its ears against its head and looks in the direction of the other animal, often emitting intermittent chattering calls, which are also heard when animals play together. When one sub-group approaches another from which it has been separated for some time, both of them may emit a high-pitched bark.

Touching or kissing the genital regions, or standing and embracing the hindquarters is directed to both infants and strangers to whom the males have stopped being aggressive. Young appear to have similar but short-lived gestures which are directed at other young and may initiate play. Grunting by all members of a troop also occurs on assembling at sleeping sites and when quietly gathered or in feeding.

Presenting and mounting in greeting

Two kinds of presentation are distinguished. Whenever the animal initiates contact by presenting with the hindquarters lowered, the sequence is not followed by the presenter being mounted. This type of behaviour occurs between adult females, when a female approaches another with an infant. While she is doing this she may be looking backwards over her shoulder, lipsmacking towards the mother. An adult male may walk quickly over to another adult male and lower his hindquarters. This is usually done by a dominant male, who initiates the sequence in this way and whose rump is then grasped by the other animal. This type of behaviour appears to take place when there is little tension and excitement between the participants. On the other hand, presenting which is followed by mounting by the other animal appears in situations where the excitement is much higher, when the contact may be initiated by either member of the pair. When presenting occurs as the initiation of the contact, it may be done at several yards' distance; the further it is, the more the tension between the animals concerned. This type of presentation and mounting reflects the rank order within the group; when there is a clearly dominant male all other males present to him, but he does not do so to them.

The gelada baboon (Plate 6)

The gelada baboon, *Theropithecus gelada*, studied by J. H. Crook,[13] is a ground-dwelling vegetarian like the rest of the baboons, inhabiting mainly areas in Ethiopia, notably the Semyen highlands, which rise to over five thousand metres above sea level. They are dramatically sculptured into enormous gorges, belonging either to the Blue Nile or to the Tandazze river systems, which produce long escarpments of tremendous height and grandeur. In the east and north they fade away into the lowlands and eventually into the Danakil desert. The highlands have a temperate climate with a dry season from September to June.

The gelada lives in herds of up to four hundred animals, foraging back and forth along the edges of the gorges and some distance into the hinterland, especially when the rains increase the food supply. During this season the herds move as single units, with the females predominating near the cliff edge and surrounded by males, both adult and subadult, which form a protection against attack from the predators roaming the uplands. Whenever danger threatens, the whole troop moves towards the cliff edge and the females and young descend first down the cliff faces on to the ledges, the males continuing to act as a shield above them. The troop also sleeps on these cliff ledges.

This simple structure, however, hides a more complex composition, which Crook uncovered only after being able to recognize individual animals. Then he found that the single troop was made up of one-male groups, as encountered in the hamadryas, mingled with members of male bands, the majority of whose members moved together on the periphery of the troop. The existence of these components became evident in the dry season when the food was less plentiful; and then the male bands, varying in number between 4 and 12 (averaging 7 to 8), separated out from one another and moved farther away from the one-male groups, which also tended to separate out in smaller groups along the cliff edge. These two major sections occasionally mingled for short periods. Unlike the hamadryas, however, when the geladas come together in large herds the one-male group becomes totally intermingled with the rest of the herd. Crook found that the females of a one-male group, although often widely separated, periodically gathered close to their male and appeared to interact sexually only with him. There is a tendency for the group of females to move with their babies synchronously with their male and independently, to some extent, of other members of the herd. Thus they remain distinct over long periods of time and no females were lost from any of these groups under observation. When, however, the members of a one-male group have become separated, an adult male of one of these groups may periodically draw himself up into a 'haughty', puffed-up posture and look around him for his females, which often then gather round him if they are near by. If some of them are farther away, the male may occasionally charge through the herd, directing his charge at one of his distant females and scattering others in his path, coming to a halt on all fours with the female screaming and posturing in front of him. When he returns, she will follow him back. This situation is clearly analogous to the neck-bite of the hamadryas baboon.

Although in the Semyen district shooting no doubt artificially depleted the number of adult males – which are the most prominent and also the boldest animals in a herd – the sex ratio in herds shows a considerable predominance of females, varying from about 2·5 to 1 to 7 to 1, the males in the all-male groups being insufficient to account for the difference in the population as a whole.

As in the hamadryas, forward movement of a group of this kind is initiated by the males, an increasing number of individuals rising and striding forward, taking food as they go. After three hundred metres or so, they settle down and start feeding and there is a general movement of monkeys following them, feeding, grooming and moving. As an animal very rarely passes one which is already sitting down, the movement of the group tends to stop at the place where the male leaders are, and is dependent upon their initiative in moving forward to the next stage. In the general movement, however, it is clear that males move more frequently, farther and range outward from the cliff more than females. This greater activity accounts for their relative positions on the ground and their role in activating movement. Their daily range is anything from one and a half to four and a half miles. A single herd, which was observed for three days, travelled five miles, leaving pockets of monkeys behind to sleep on cliff edges which are preferred sleeping sites, especially when they have overhangs and prominences. The members of the herd were scattered about in these places for the night, but no detailed study was made of the group in which they slept.

Herds do not as a rule return to sleep in the same positions, and numbers counted on a given ledge on twelve successive nights ranged from nothing on two occasions to one hundred on the most densely packed occasion. The information at present available is insufficient to determine whether there are ranges with core areas other than those which arise from the provision of particularly suitable sleeping places at particular points.

The hamadryas baboon (Plate 7)

In 1957 Hans Kummer[14] published a very detailed study of the colony of fifteen hamadryas baboons living in a sunken open enclosure (46' by 82') in the Zurich Zoo. At that time the adults comprised a dominant male and four females, three subadult males and two young males and five females between one and three years old.

Kummer's approach stemmed directly from the work of Carpenter and Tinbergen, and he set out both to define and list the elements of behaviour and to obtain some idea of the structure of the social relations within the group. At the same time he allowed himself to select on the basis of what he saw; to allow his mind to abstract the underlying pattern from his awareness of the group. He saw that the agonistic elements of social behaviour and the mother/infant relationship stood out. His subsequent studies in the wild, with which we are here mainly concerned, confirmed the insight he gained from this captive colony into the precise nature of the way the infant's early relation to the mother is transferred into its adult social relations. Much of his early study borrows heavily from traditional terms for labelling the behaviour, the exact nature of which is, however, clear from his description.

Armed with a precise knowledge of much of the repertoire of this species, Kummer and Kurt[15] studied the wild hamadryas in eastern Ethiopia between November 1960 and October 1961. After surveying a region north-east of Addis Ababa occupied by twenty-three different populations, they chose for detailed observation a representative population living in relatively open country, away from any cultivated land, where baboons were not likely to be shot as vermin.

The hamadryas baboons sleep in parties on ledges of vertical rock faces varying in height from ten to thirty metres and always approach these sleeping sites from above along narrow pathways which require all the adult's skill to negotiate. The sleeping parties vary in size from 12 to 750 individuals and contain 18 per cent adult males and 33 per cent adult females. The number of individuals in these parties changes almost every night. In the morning the party leaves as a whole, but soon splits up into smaller bands varying in size from 5 to 40 individuals. These bands may lose contact with each other during the day and appear to re-collect with others at the same or different sleeping rocks on the following night.

On the basis of the three following clearly defined criteria the one-male group was found to be the only social unit of constant composition:

1. the spatial distribution of the individuals,
2. the frequency and types of interaction among particular individuals, differing in frequency and type from those with other individuals, and
3. the length of time for which these persist.

One to four (rarely as many as nine) females and their offspring up to eighteen months of age follow a single adult male. Outside these groups, but closely attached to them, live the juvenile and subadult males and some adult males without females. Occasionally, adult males remain solitary during the day. Observed for ten weeks, the composition of eight groups was changed in that time only by the addition of young born to the females, and, in one instance, by the loss of a female.

In contrast to the absence of any stable relationship between the units themselves and to the lack of any prominent order of dominance between the adult males of the different units even when they are together in a band, the adult males themselves form a stable relation to other members of this unit and are the centre around which their females and young cluster, so that on average they are, at any one time, not more than two feet away when stationary and nine feet when on the move. This strict coherence is brought about by the females following the male wherever he goes. If the female drops behind, the male stares at her with outstretched head, and this is usually sufficient to make her run towards him, screaming and with the mane on her back raised. If she remains away too long or

F

strays too far off, interacts with, or allows an outsider to come between them, he rushes at her, gives her a neck-bite and then she follows him.

This aggregation of the members of a unit can be seen to involve, and may be the result of, the way members confine their attention within the group, so that for adults most of their social contacts are made within it despite the close proximity of neighbouring units while assembling at or leaving the sleeping cliffs.

At the sleeping rock every adult member will find close to it as many strangers as members of its own group, yet a member of a unit will choose a social partner within the unit four hundred times more often than it will choose an individual outside it. This means that not only is the attention of subordinate members turned inwards, but that much of the adult males' social attention is on his females. This fact may reduce the amount of attention the adult males give to each other and may be the main reason for the absence of rank order between them, thus freeing the social bonds deployed in the male rank orders of other baboons and so enabling the separate hamadryas units to fluctuate in their associations with others.

Fights between females attached to different males do not occur as they do in the savannah baboons, and on the rare occasions of agonistic encounters between the females of a one-male group the fighting is always done by enlisting the support of the male. The fragmentation of the troop into one-male units is only fully realized among the adults. Infants, juveniles and subadult males are not herded by the adult males and make contact throughout the troop, showing patterns of organization very similar to those of the savannah baboons. Infants and juveniles from different one-male units meet and form a play group. Juvenile males and females set up a temporary consort relationship with any member of the same age group from anywhere in the troop, the female leaving its unit for the time being and entering into the sexual consort relation with a juvenile male. If a subadult male has not yet formed a one-male unit of his own, it remains loosely attached to another unit, sometimes groomed by an adult female of that unit but rarely having a chance to copulate.

In the savannah baboons both sexes participate in play groups until the age of three years, after which the females join female groups, while the males' play becomes rougher and an increasing dominance element develops. In the hamadryas the play group is made up mostly of males up to three years of age, and a predominance of males is already evident in the play groups of the five-month-old infants, when male infants leave their mothers more often than do the females, who rarely appear in the play groups after one year old. After this, the young female becomes the object of attention of a young adult male of about three years old which has had no female, and which incorporates the female into its one-male unit. The subadult male tends to kidnap and hug infants, and the young adult male permanently adopts and hugs juveniles. As this mothering by the male fades, its retrieving behaviour is gradually replaced by the ritualized neck-bite on the female's nape or back. At about this time also sexual behaviour replaces hugging the female and the adult male unit is established out of components transformed and transferred to another individual from the original mother/infant pattern. The young female fails to conceive for the next year and a half, by which time she is physically mature. Incorporation of females into the one-male unit therefore appears to be the result of an attention-binding mechanism dependent on active aggression on the part of the male, to whom the subordinate females subsequently run for protection at an age when in the *cynocephalus* baboon societies the adolescent would have run into the arms of a member of the same age group.

Relations between adult males

In addition to the one-male unit, the formation of which we have already discussed, there are three other forms of grouping which involve the association of a number of adult males of the one-male units or of such a male with a subadult male. They are:

1. The two-male team, which is an association of an adult with his unit and a subadult, with or without his females.
2. A band, which appears to be an association of adult males with their units, up to a maximum number of approximately 80 individuals.
3. The sleeping troop, which is a temporary association of a number of bands and may comprise as many as 750 individuals.

We will now consider the relationships between the males in these different groupings.

As juveniles, young males come together in groups, and when the young male becomes subadult he may sit in this group, but does not participate in its activities. More and more of the time he attaches himself to one of the one-male units, thus constituting a two-male unit.

This subordinate at first only engages in furtive sexual and grooming relations with females of the group, but later these are replaced by interactions in which the leader of the unit presents to the subordinate before changing direction in an effort to make him follow. The followers of a number of neighbouring one-male units may frequently interact with each other, especially in a form of presenting to each other, an activity which heralds the imminent departure of the presenting male. This behaviour is taken over into the next stage of the young male's development. At first, this young adult, perhaps followed by a female or two (the start of his one-male unit) follows behind the older member of the two-male team. Whenever the older member wishes to change direction, he presents to the younger one. As the younger one matures, roles are gradually reversed, more and more of the initiative for the movement being taken by the rapidly maturing younger one. Such two-male teams could be regarded as a means of acquainting the young males with the nature of the terrain. The two-male teams are observed after the bands and troops have broken up mostly into one-male units, during the day's foraging. The one-male unit and the two-male team are phenomena of the widely scattered foraging activities of this baboon, living in a much less productive country than does the savannah baboon, which remains together in troops for the whole of the day.

The difference between the bands and the troops is to be seen much more clearly during the activity which brings animals together at the sleeping sites or cliffs than at any other time. At these sites the troop size varies inversely with the number of available cliffs, and in Diredawa, where only one such cliff exists, a troop of 750 individuals occupied it every night. When resting, the animals did not segregate into smaller parties and no aggression took place, but in the morning the troop broke up. The same tolerance seemed to exist between parties of baboons which slept on alternate nights on two cliffs about five miles apart. But, in contrast, on a single

84

occasion when a troop from ten miles away wanted to enter a cliff face which was already occupied by its usual tenants, the newcomers waited for half an hour before finally retiring to their own locality. In a third locality, two cliffs only one and a half miles apart were regularly occupied by separate parties. When on one occasion the party from one cliff wanted to sleep with the party from the other cliff, fighting broke out between the two. During this fighting the two parties broke up into four or five bands, consisting of from about 20 to 90 individuals each. Two of these bands fought while the remainder occupied neighbouring ridges and hills. These observations suggest that the band consists of a number of individual adult males who have a high degree of tolerance of each other's presence and that some lesser tolerance exists between a number of bands who only occasionally share the same sleeping site and thereby, in the mornings and evenings, constitute a troop.

To summarize: it appears that a number of bands come together at a single sleeping site, or alternate between a number of sites which are shared by the same group of bands; they form, in effect, a group of familiar individuals, which start the day as one or two troops, depending on the number of sites occupied by them. These break up as the day goes on and the animals disperse more widely into one-male units and two-male teams, which may be made up of two such units. When gathered together into bands, the one-male unit remains nevertheless a spatially distinct entity, but the spatial distribution of the males which form the centres of these units throughout the band is very similar to that observed in the savannah baboons.

Female assemblies of hamadryas baboons in the form in which they are seen in other societies are not present by virtue of the structure of the one-male unit.

The band is the only other social group showing some elements of cohesion, since bands and not troops fight each other, and the males within a band are known to each other individually; this probably constitutes the binding element within the band. Hence, the relationship between adult males may be similar to that in the cohorts of other societies. We have noted that clusters of young hardly have time to form before the females are abducted; soon afterwards some juvenile males become part of a two-male team.

The langur (Plate 8)

The common langur of India (*Presbytis entellus*), is a long-legged monkey with a specialized stomach adapted for digesting large quantities of mature leaves of low food value, such as are found on the vegetation in seasonally arid country. Langurs are also able to live for months without drinking water, supplementing their leafy diet with buds, fruit and other more succulent additions. Their diet restricts them to the neighbourhood of large trees, to which each individual of the group returns for safety. The group returns at night to the trees to sleep in the branches. They are found up to eight thousand feet from sea level.

Phyllis Jay[16] studied langur social behaviour in the forests of Lorcha in Central India and in more open cultivated country at Kaukori near Lucknow in the north. Jay, by gradually moving closer each day and staying near the Kaukori langurs as they moved about, was eventually able to sit among the members of the group. As she says, '... whenever an animal threatened, I turned and moved away, as is characteristic of subordinates, and never returned the threat. My rapport with the group depended in part on my subordinate posture and refusal to interact with group members.' Thus she was able to observe from as advantageous a position as any observer has yet achieved but, at the same time, she was too involved in the group to be able to see what the group was doing. The ease with which individual behaviour differences as well as appearance could be seen at close quarters was a great help in identifying all the individuals in a group of 50, even from as far off as 50 to 75 yards.

Langur groups vary in size from 5 to 120 individuals, the size of the group depending on the nature of the terrain. The number of males in the heterosexual group varies from 2 to 6, with an adult female/male ratio of between 5 to 1 and 2 to 1. Bachelor bands of up to 10 males exist, sometimes overlapping the range of the heterosexual groups. Lone males were also encountered.

Each heterosexual group occupies a range over which its members feed, frequently overlapping the range of another group at water sources. Each range contains a number of core areas where the group is found most frequently. The core areas are grouped round the sleeping trees, and the group shifts between these areas according to season. Bachelor bands appear to avoid contact with the bisexual groups and are driven off when they meet.

Jay obtained quantities of information about the amount of agonistic and grooming activity among the different classes of individuals. A high level of agonistic behaviour is found reciprocally between adult males and subadult males; mainly low-level agonistic behaviour occurs between adult male and adult female and overlaps with reciprocal grooming relations; adult males and females groom, but are not groomed by juveniles. Finally between adult females, infants and subadult females there is a very active reciprocal grooming, but no agonistic behaviour. The details of social relations suggest an agonistic bond between the adult and subadult males, despite the peripheral position of the latter, and a mixed type of bond linking the female/infant groups to the adult males.

Within the female/infant groups reciprocal grooming relations are frequent and are probably associated with the sharing of infants between females, who take them from their consenting mothers. (Similar behaviour would amount to stealing babies in the macaque groups, where mothers are antagonistic towards one another and attempt to keep off approaching females and thus retain exclusive possession of their babies.)

It is not possible to decide whether or not there is a separate spatially distinct core, comprising the most dominant adult males, although they appear to form a stable rank order. This is because Phyllis Jay's concern – like that of so many observers – is as much with defining the functional outcomes of the behaviour as with the form of the behaviour itself and, inevitably, the two become confused unless functional interpretations are left until the pattern as a whole has become clear.

Nevertheless, the essence of Jay's main thesis clearly indicates that it is the direction and object of attention that determines the form of an animal's behaviour.

It is important and revealing to recognize that the langur is a relatively large, lithe, long-limbed monkey, moving in large graceful bounds which, in an emergency, take each individual back to the safety of near-by trees. *Escape* to the safety of the trees is possible because of their persistent attention to this feature of the environment.

Jay says: '... they dash up into the nearest tree instead of depending for protection on large adult males with well-developed fighting prowess.' As this is couched in functional terms referring to the outcome, the fact that it is the *direction* of attention that is crucial does not emerge clearly. Describing behaviour by reference to its functional outcome can therefore obscure its form.

During her life among the langurs Jay became aware of the importance of their spatial arrangement, and she noticed that individuals have what she calls a 'personal space'. This phenomenon was recognized by Chance in 1956[17] in the captive colony of Indian macaques at the London Zoo and given the name of 'social space'. Avoidance of one animal by another, as Jay points out clearly, is at least as important in assessing rank as is approach: 'Reduction of all dominance interactions to numbers of successes and failures is only a partial reflection of the dominance structure and needs qualification. Patterns of social interaction most difficult to evaluate such as avoidance, are extremely important in understanding dominance.' The evidence suggests that the young male langur, like other primates, has a strong built-in approach tendency towards adult males, which is less easy to distinguish in the adult. This may be because it is suppressed in the adult in favour of an escape tendency towards the nearest trees. Thus this tendency, apparently absent in the adult, is only overlaid by the more species-specific behaviour in the adult male of the heterosexual group, for it reasserts itself in the bachelor bands.

Nevertheless, in the description of the role of the adult males of the heterosexual groups Jay emphasizes that they are 'extremely important to the maintenance of group unity and stability', so that apparently each individual's direction of flight is not solely dependent on the nearest available tree cover, but rapid bounding strides take it to where the rest of the group flees. Perhaps because of the absence of a compelling deflection of attention towards individual dominant males, their display behaviour is exaggerated and takes the form of dashing about in the treetops, whooping all the while, the whoop being a 'quick and effective way of gathering a group together in the forest, where visibility is poor'. This would suggest that the display behaviour of males already in the trees reinforces the escape of the rest of the group by adding a focus of attention, which directs the fleeing members of the group. In this way group cohesion could be achieved in the face of danger. More concern with the nature of sociability, however, will be required before the reasons for group cohesion can be fully understood.

In conclusion, it looks as if the langur society shares all the adult features of other centripetal subhuman primate groups: female assemblages and male cohorts in the form of bachelor bands. In the juvenile cluster the behaviour of the young early shows the sex differentiation which is suppressed in the males of the heterosexual group, as described in Chapter 4.

Langur groups appear relaxed, with a low incidence of agonistic relations and a high incidence of grooming, but episodes of fighting occur between adult males and subadult males, and during these the females with their young separate from the males until the fighting has died down. Agonistic social gestures increase in intensity in the following order of gestures, with slight differences between the sexes when adult: tensing, staring at, a slap on the ground, grimace, crouch and stand suddenly, bite in the air, and toss head; then – and these are high intensity responses – lunge but remain in place, chase, hit and slap, bite, wrestle. The responses to these by a subordinate are, again in increasing order of intensity: avoid visual contact, turn head and look away, turn back, move tongue in and out of mouth, grimace, embrace, walk away, present, combined grimace and turning back or presenting and running away.

Group splitting and sub-group formation

The Japanese school of primatologists have, more than any other group of workers, devoted their energies to long-term determination of group composition. This has been carried out not only on the Japanese macaque in its native habitat near to where the workers live, but also on the langur in India.

Itani,[18] in more than ten years of observation, has watched the Takasakiyama group of Japanese macaques nearly treble its size from 200 to more than 550 and ultimately split into a major and minor group. This process was also watched by Sugiyama.[19] The leader of the minor group was one of the leaders of the subadult males in the original group, around whom a number of females had begun to congregate at the periphery. The processes involved in this separation, however, were not clearer than this.

On the other hand, a very detailed account has been given of a change in the social structure of a troop of the common langur in India which took a fortnight to complete, also observed during a two-year study by Sugiyama.[20] Langur populations are made up of one-male heterosexual groups and separate male cohorts. The following instance records the change brought about in a heterosexual one-male group possessing 9 adult females, 1 subadult male, 5 juvenile males and 3 juvenile females and 5 infants, which was the largest group in the area (24 animals). This group was attacked and disrupted by a neighbouring cohort of males which, under the leadership of its own dominant male, first coalesced with the heterosexual group. The cohort then drove out the male overlord of the group together with the juveniles, and the group was reconstituted with the dominant cohort male taking over the role of the male overlord and driving away the rest of the cohort males. The process, however, was one of a complex series of interactions; among them was a phase of disorganization of the original one-male group by threats from the male cohort, accompanied by the withdrawal of a few of the adult females which were surrounded at times by these cohort males and had to defend themselves. This was a period of great excitement, accompanied by sexual presentation (without copulation) by one of the females, who ultimately became the consort of the new overlord. The original overlord then counter-attacked and re-established his authority, only to be defeated twice in single combat with the dominant cohort male. After this the females abandoned their young which joined up with the old overlord, the females going to the new dominant male and his consort. The final process involved the driving away of the rest of the cohort males, leaving the new overlord in possession of the females. Now the group consisted of the new dominant male, 9 adult females and 2 juvenile females (12 animals). The new troop inherited the whole of the home range of the old heterosexual group. The cohort males returned to their habit of moving about between the areas occupied by the heterosexual groups.

Sexual behaviour
'Perineal swelling or sexual skin does not occur in langurs and the female initiates sexual behavior by displaying three gestures not

associated as a sequence in any other social context – only the sexually receptive female simultaneously shakes her head, drops her tail on the ground and presents to adult males.

'Sexual behavior actually plays a very small part in the life of an adult female. She is pregnant for approximately six months and is not sexually receptive again until her infant is weaned at from ten to twelve months of age; she will not give birth again for another six to eight months. Births in many areas are spaced at approximately two-year intervals. When a female is not in oestrus, adult males show no sexual interest in her.

'Although oestrus females do not solicit males in any particular order, there is a tendency for the most dominant males to consort with oestrus females at the height of their activity at the middle of the oestrus period: the time at which ovulation and conception probably occur.'[21]

The patas monkey (Plate 9)

The patas is a ground-based monkey, very like the langur in size, build and general appearance, and it lives in forest and open country, close to trees, bordering the northern equatorial and tropical zones of Africa, extending from near the coast in the west to as far as the upper Nile in the east. Its range overlaps that of the baboons, extending (especially into arid areas) well to the north of them.

The study of the wild patas monkey, *Erythrocebus patas* in Uganda was undertaken by K. R. L. Hall.[22]

Method of observation

The solution of the problem of observing the patas monkey lay in keeping contact with, and following, a group for as long as possible. The group was followed on foot, and the observer retraced his steps to a Land Rover left at the nearest point to the rest site of the previous night. Binoculars were used on all occasions. Chart bearings, charts and aerial photographs were used to construct maps of the home ranges.

Two observers simultaneously noted the positions of neighbouring groups and plotted their successive day ranges. Other groups were never encountered in the same locality at one time, despite the presence of two separate groups in neighbouring areas. This was

established by one observer following one group, while another simultaneously located fresh spoor in the range of a neighbouring group.

The patas move about in groups, which vary in size from 9 to 30
animals. As no group contains more than 1 adult male plus 1 or 2
young males, the adult sex ratio varies from 4 to 1 to 12 to 1, probably
the highest ratio of ♀ : ♂ in any primate group. Extra males live
isolated or in bachelor bands, not as peripheral males loosely
attached to one of the groups.

A seasonal birth peak made recognition of age classes possible for
the first three years of life. After this it is difficult to determine age,
but the differential growth rate between the sexes establishes sex
distinctions.

Each group occupies a home range. During the midday siesta the
members of a group rest together in trees; if alarmed during the day
they run out of the trees into open ground. Their resting habits at
night are different. As evening approaches, and while the adult male
is reconnoitring far afield, other members disperse by twos and threes
into widely scattered trees, with an average density of only one
monkey per hectare. Associated with this habit, the resting sites are
never the same for two nights in succession within the home range,
which covers about 5,200 hectares. These habits of dispersal within
the resting sites and their irregular location are an integral part of the
patas's protective behaviour, based on exploiting the various modes
of escape and concealment.

Like the langur, the patas can survive with very little water. The
diet of the patas consists mainly of grasses, seeds, seed pods, fruit and
berries and – to a small extent – leaves, supplemented by lizards,
insects and fungi. The patas feeds by searching ahead as it moves at
a steady walk over the ground, picking up food in one hand. It will
stand on hind legs and hold a branch in one hand to pick off edible
parts with the other. Sometimes it swipes at and catches passing
insects. It will pounce on lizards and grasshoppers, but does not pull
up roots or break off branches. During all this activity the patas are
well spread out, coming together only at places where their choice
food – mushrooms – are to be found. A new area is often surveyed
for as long as fifteen minutes by the adult male from a promontory
before he rejoins the waiting group, which only then moves into it.

The wide dispersion of the members of a group throughout its daytime activity undoubtedly serves as a means of defence, for the male always keeps well away from the rest of the group, allowing the females and young (which crouch and remain immobile) to remain concealed while he carries out a diversionary display when necessary. The adult male possesses white haunches with a light blue contrasting scrotum and is much larger than the female. This makes him very conspicuous during the diversionary display, which he starts by jumping high in the air, and, if bushes and boulders are near by, he jumps with all fours against them, bouncing back in a startling manner. He follows this by a zig-zag retreat so as to place the intruder between himself and the rest of the group to lure it away. Whenever possible, however, the defence of the group as a whole is based on escape by very fast running.

The dispersal pattern is maintained during drinking, the females staying behind while the adult male surveys the area from a promontory. After he has descended to drink at a water-hole he will be joined by the rest of the group. No member, however, stays to drink for more than half a minute. Moreover, water-holes are frequently by-passed. Probably sufficient water is obtained from dew, but wherever holes in trees contain water the animals dip their hands and arms into them and lick the fur or cup their fingers.

Pattern of daily activities

The absence of any worked-out method for recording the daily pattern of activity has led to a somewhat undifferentiated picture of the behaviour throughout the day. In most species this appears to consist of a morning and afternoon peak of activity with a midday two-hour siesta. Hall, however, has shown that among the patas each component activity presents a distinct pattern in relation to the distance travelled during the day.

Feeding: a morning and afternoon peak was observed only when the distance travelled was large.

Social grooming: this activity rose sharply in the first two hours after sunrise and remained constant until it disappeared three hours before nightfall, when movement had become minimal.

Social play: this rose rapidly to a peak and gradually declined throughout the day whenever the distance travelled was small, but was otherwise grouped round the rest periods.

A clue to the interpretation of this pattern is provided by a study of young antelopes, where play does not increase in intensity or duration following prolonged interruption, but appears to be related to the amount of time available and energy to spare which is used up whenever other more directed activities supervene; Hall's observations of the distribution of play in the behaviour of the young patas is in accord with this interpretation.

Play is initiated by one youngster bouncing up and down on all fours on one spot, glancing towards a playmate. A play chase follows until the chased youngster is caught, when both animals start wrestling, grasping with the hands on shoulders and arms, both rolling over on the ground. Slapping with hands may precede much biting and wrestling. Then, finally, there is the play bounce in which the young patas hurls himself sideways as he continues to run away.

Relations within the group

Actual fighting has not been observed amongst the patas and they have no submission posture – presentation has not been seen in captivity or in the wild. A threatened animal moves away or flees. An aggressor walks towards another animal, looking straight at it. If this is alternated with glances at other animals in an attempt to solicit support, a low 'huh-huh' noise is invariably given. A quick swipe with the hand will elicit retreat, or occasionally a female will pounce on another in a sudden attack, giving it a quick nip, which again sends the victim off in flight. All these gestures are brief, a chase not going farther than fifty metres.

The adult patas male, unlike the baboon, does not attack females who may threaten or attack mothers or infants in the group.

While the form of these agonistic encounters clearly shows that there is no balanced agonistic behaviour, the relatively infrequent occurrence of these encounters is also notable. Only 49 episodes were noted in 627 hours, and only 10 of these involved physical contact. All agonistic episodes occurred in three situations:

1. A mother towards an animal playing roughly with her infant.
2. During aggregation over preferred food. Here adult females have priority. These females sometimes chase other monkeys until they drop their food, but no fighting and little counter-threat occurs.
3. A sexually interested male towards harassers.

94

Sexual behaviour is confined to the months of July to September, and is initiated by active sociability on the part of the females, shown by a cringing half-run towards the male, followed by her sitting with her back to him, arched forward, and then turning to look at him with puffed cheek pouches. In captivity, sexual soliciting is accompanied by a low chortling, but this is inaudible beyond six metres, and is thus unobtrusive and will not endanger the animals.

Grooming, although not frequent (approximately one action per hour), takes place when the group is together in a tree or tarries round a prominent position such as a termite mound. Females are involved mostly, and it is not clear whether young males also participate. The adult male is never in these groups, though one or two females may groom him during rest periods. He rarely and only briefly reciprocates or initiates grooming of them.

The proportion of grooming initiated by one sex towards the other is exactly as in baboon groups. Lipsmacking, glancing towards and away may accompany the approach of the one soliciting grooming, which continually sits with its back towards the prospective groomer. Sometimes the soliciting monkey presses so hard with its back against the other that it pushes him over.

In all these descriptions certain elements of behaviour appear in a number of different types of activity. Bouncing, for example, occurs:

1. as an invitation to play,
2. when pouncing on food,
3. during the diversionary display of the male,
4. during escape running,
5. in the pouncing of one female attacking another,

and is an element in escape behaviour. The full significance of bouncing and other typical features will be discussed in Chapter 6.

Hall's observations reveal that in the societies of this monkey female assemblies are identifiable, and the male cohorts exist as bachelor bands, but nowhere in his description is there any mention of a sub-group which could be taken to refer to juvenile clusters. Since he is not primarily concerned with the structure of the society, it is difficult to say whether they are present.

The gibbon (Plate 10)

The gibbons are classified among the apes. Together with the siamang they stand anatomically in many respects between the great apes and the catarrhine monkeys (the macaques, baboons and langurs). On the other hand, the gibbon's mode of life in the trees has meant that much of its behaviour is very different from the other apes.

The opposable thumb in the gibbon is separated from the other four digits by a deep cleft (absent in the other apes), and gives it a sure grip on branches (although the thumb is not used in brachiation). This enables it to hang by its long, freely articulated arms, with which it swings under the branches – a form of progression known as brachiating. Because of its light weight the gibbon is able to swing out from smaller terminal branches of one tree to those of the next. This enables it to feed on the terminal branches of trees, and provides an effective method of escape in the dense forest as none of its predators can follow this arboreal route. The gibbon is fully adapted to arboreal life; 90 per cent of its life is spent below the upper canopy of the trees.

C. R. Carpenter,[23] accompanied by Sherwood Washburn, studied the gibbon's behaviour in north Thailand in the neighbourhood of Chiengmai, and found that it was essential to exploit man-made paths through the forest in order to get a clear view of these tree-living apes. They set out to observe individuals and groups for long periods of time, and to record and report their observations. Various means were used:

1. A group was located along the wall of the forest, at the edge of a clearing, by picking up the direction of their calls on a parabolic reflector. They could then follow this group unobserved for several hours.
2. Gibbons are sacred to Buddhists and at Doi Dao, a Buddhist holy place 1,400 feet above sea level, they found them unmolested and used to the presence of man. Food was plentiful even in the months of March, April and May, when many of the trees lose their leaves and it was easier to keep them under observation.
3. Direct and continuous observation of one group was supplemented

96

by observation from 'blinds' constructed at strategic points near food-trees and water sources.

4. The movement of groups was also noted from cliff faces, hill tops and tall trees.

The value of having *two* trained observers for ensuring the accuracy of reports by cross-checking was soon recognized. It was during this study that Carpenter became aware of the need to observe the behaviour of the individual and the behaviour of individuals in a group as two distinct dimensions of the social life. This distinction has subsequently become of great theoretical as well as practical importance.

The gibbon (*Hylobates lar*) group varies in size from two to six individuals, with a modal number of four. Each group could be recognized by the size and colour composition of its members – these gibbons are buff-and-white and black-and-white. The same group was found repeatedly in the same trees, and later the existence of a limited area within which the group remained was established by following a group round throughout the day for several days.

Each group was located early in the morning when, on waking, the gibbons call loudly to each other. John Ellefson[24] reports that defended territories range from 40 to 300 acres in size. Neighbouring groups are always antagonists and occupy territories with a 10 to 20 per cent overlap. He noted that a young male intruding into the region of overlap often 'calls' loudly, and such males, if alone, may be chased back some distance into their own territory. Eighty-five per cent of the gibbons's time is spent foraging, and they retire to sleep in one of a number of preferred trees. There are roughly ten to twelve individuals in two or three groups within a square mile.

Intra-group squabbling over food is prevalent. The primary mechanism promoting the expulsion of maturing young is harsh treatment of young by parents in feeding situations. Expulsion holds group size at or below six individuals. Lone males were frequently seen in association with a group (but not being part of it), or making exploratory approaches to neighbouring groups. As older males are tolerated within a group, it is likely that these lone males were young adults. The equal sex ratio of the family groups suggests that these

G

young males must be considered as in a transitional phase between leaving their family group and joining up with a female to form a new family group, though this has not been observed.

Group composition

This species is an example where the adults do not form female assemblies and male cohorts, but some of Ellefson's observations suggest that the immature animals of neighbouring groups are attracted, even if antagonistically, towards one another.

The gorilla (Plate 11)

The social life of the mountain gorilla was first studied by Emlen and Schaller in 1959, and the study was continued by Schaller[25] alone in the following year. The gorilla is the largest of the apes and can weigh as much as 450 lbs when adult.

Habitat and feeding habits

Succulent plants abound in the mountain rain forests, providing the gorillas with tasty morsels from selected parts of vines, barks, roots, some fruits and certain leaves which they pluck and hold with their hands while they are eating.

The mountain gorilla may be found in the mountain rain forests in the *hagenia* woodland, or on open slopes of giant lobelias, at a height of up to 13,000 feet where the temperature falls to zero on occasions. But three-quarters of the gorilla population are found in the valleys where the temperatures remain around 21 degrees Centigrade.

Method of observation

Their habitat makes prolonged observation difficult, but in the *hagenia* woodland at the Kabara study area, between the peaks of the Virunga volcanoes north of Lake Kivu, the absence of shrubs made prolonged observation possible. In this region Schaller made his observations by following a group of gorillas until he was accepted by them. Continuous observation of one group lasted only so long as that group remained within the Kabara area (never more than seven hours because the gorillas frequently return to the forests).

Group structure and composition

The population is divided into groups varying in size from 5 to 27 individuals, each group moving at an irregular rate within its own range. A typical range varies in extent between 10 and 15 square miles.

The types of individuals composing a group were distinguished and divided into five classes, as follows:

1. an infant is carried for long periods of time from birth until about three years old. (This was ascertained by study of captive gorillas.) At the end of infancy it weighs from 50–60 lbs, when it becomes
2. a juvenile until the age of six, by which time it has doubled its weight. After the age of six
3. the *females* are fully grown and may be seen with their young. It is known from the study of captive gorillas that the *male* reaches sexual maturity and adult size later than the female, i.e. at about nine years of age, when he weighs about 250 lbs.
4. *Males* between the age of six and ten years are *black-backed*.
5. *Males* ten years of age and older have a prominent silver saddle and are described as *silver-backed*.

The average composition of eleven groups at Kabara was

10 per cent silver-backed males
 9 per cent black-backed males
37 per cent females
17 per cent juveniles
27 per cent infants

(The apparent preponderance of adult females over males is consistent with the existence of lone males in the population and with late maturation of the males.)

The size of the gorilla groups varies considerably from place to place. There are 6 to 7 individuals in the groups inhabiting the mountain rain forest region, but they average 16 to 17 individuals (the upper limit of group size) where vegetation is mainly *hagenia* and *hypericum*. The size of the groups thus varies with the nature of the habitat, though how it influences group size is not yet known. Over the six months of observation some groups changed their composition; others did not. For example, a group could be joined by one or more males or females with infants, or such individuals could leave the group for one or two weeks. A group which underwent a considerable number of changes was observed for a year, and during that time a number of silver-backed males individually came and left the group for several weeks at a time, but all the while the dominant male remained.

The groups rarely split, and if they did so separated for short distances only and never for longer than a day.

Lone males

Lone males are a distinct and important feature of the population structure. As in the populations of Indian and Japanese macaques, where lone males are also a feature, lone females were not seen.

The average ratio of adult females to adult males within a typical group is 2 to 1, but the ratio in the whole population is 3 to 2. In Schaller's opinion this difference is not entirely made up by the counting in of lone males, but by a high post-juvenile mortality amongst males. This could be due to hazards to which lone mature males are likely to be exposed and could be, indirectly, the result of their exclusion, self-imposed or otherwise, from the group.

Schaller says that lone gorilla males freely associate with some groups, by which is meant that they wander apparently unmolested through the group. On one occasion a lone silver-backed male was threatened by the dominant male of a group as he approached, and he did not advance further. It appears that lone males which attach themselves to the outer edge of a group for one or two days are at one end of a gradation of what may be termed 'visiting' males, some of which stay for as long as several months as an integral part of the group. These 'visitors' are adult males of all ages. However, it is worth noting that out of six groups observed these 'visiting' males associated with only two.

Relation to and interaction with other groups

The mountain gorilla resembles other forest-dwelling primates in leading a wandering existence within a circumscribed range, but appears to differ strikingly from some of them (gibbons, and to some extent the chimpanzees), in lacking preference for particular tracks feeding localities or lodge sites.

Two adjacent groups can coexist over the greater proportion of the area covered by their two ranges, and the range of a third group may coincide (but only along part of its boundary) with that of the other two. This variation in the amount of overlap may result from the absence of any vocal or behavioural defence of range or, indeed, any consistent behaviour when two groups meet.

More than once two particular groups met and occupied the same area, and on one occasion constructed their nests adjacent to one another. The old males, however, kept well apart.

A group's behaviour towards another will vary from very aggressive encounters to occasions like the above, where two groups mingle. Overt antagonism between the dominant males of the groups was observed when one charged the other and both then stood glaring at each other, with eyebrow ridges almost touching one another. The mode of interaction between two groups is therefore as variable as is the extent of overlap between the ranges.

Cycle of daily activities

The gorillas sleep at night in a nest constructed on the ground or a few feet above it in trees, at different sites within their range (see Figure 6, below). After waking they spend up to an hour or two

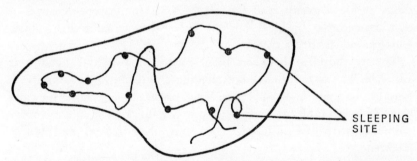

SLEEPING
SITE

FIGURE 6: Typical daily movements of a gorilla group within its range (*compare with figure 4*)

in the nest, when beating of the chest often occurs. Gorillas feed and move a little for about two hours, resting for two hours either side of midday. Their activity increases in the late afternoon, when about half the daily movement is accomplished, feeding as they go. Activity then slows until dusk, when new nests are built. Sometimes this late movement may take the group into another vegetational region without much of the available food in its path being taken.

The factors determining the amount of time spent in any one area and the rate of movement from one part of the range to another are not known, but each group moves at a different rate from day to day, while maintaining a characteristic daily mean for that group.

Relations within the group

Dominance/subordination relation in behaviour is evident in four distinct ways:

1. A subordinate will step aside from the path of a more dominant animal while on the trail.
2. A dominant will supplant a subordinate at some preferred site, such as a shady tree.
3. Rapid movement of a more dominant animal towards another will temporarily make the subordinate desist from some activity, but this may be resumed later.
4. A dominant animal will bat another with its arm and thereby force it to withdraw, e.g. female with young towards a female trying to touch her baby.

There is a linear order of rank between different classes of individuals within a group, and the silver-backed males are followed in dominance order by black-backed males, then females with young, females and, finally, juveniles.

The relationship between black-backed males and females is variable. The order of rank between females is unstable, as has been found in baboons and macaques. Size appears to determine the rank order between males and, as this is partly a function of age, the order coincides with the difference between silver-backed and black-backed.

Copulation

Copulation is performed in a variety of positions during the same period of copulation, which was seen to last for a quarter of an hour in one instance, and in the presence of another male. This is unlike the short, stereotyped mountings typical of the baboon and macaque. In captive gorillas, Schaller saw much chasing, wrestling and fondling preceding copulation, which was sometimes performed in the ventro-ventral position. This behaviour is therefore much more varied in form, prolonged and relaxed than in baboons and macaques.

Grooming

The general social interaction rate for gorillas is much lower than for macaques. Although gorillas were not often seen to groom each other, the frequency was slightly greater than the frequency of agonistic interaction. Taken together, these two types of behaviour accounted for a large proportion of the total interactions. This proportion is substantially the same as that found for a captive colony of rhesus macaques at the Whipsnade Gardens of the London Zoo, except that the gorilla does not groom reciprocally and in this appears to be unique.

Infants older than six months groom others, in this respect differing from macaques which do not groom until they are adult. Self-grooming is very common, especially among the females. At times juveniles initiate social contact by grooming.

Grooming is concentrated on parts of the body easily accessible to the animal itself. Soliciting for grooming is not mentioned by Schaller. He classified the frequency of grooming with age and sex classes and found an inverse correlation with age. Since position in the rank order reflects the age and size of the individual, this relation of grooming to social status may be the same as that found by Reynolds for the Whipsnade colony of rhesus monkeys where grooming frequency was inversely related to status.

Group cohesion and attention structure

Schaller found the gorilla groups 'quite cohesive' but, in his opinion, it is not yet understood how group cohesion comes about. To enable us to make generalizations about similarities and differences of groups of different species we must consider the spatial organization of the group and also what is meant by being 'quite cohesive'.

The members of a gorilla group stick together over long periods of time, so that the diameter of the group rarely exceeds two hundred feet and, except for extra visiting males, single individuals are not usually more than one hundred feet from other members of the group.

Schaller describes a 'central core' of the group as composed of the dominant male and all females and young surrounded by a varying number of peripheral males; this spatial organization tended to function in much the same way by day and at sleeping sites.

Schaller does not suggest that the dominant male occupies a spatially central position, for he notes that while the group is moving the position of the dominant male depends on the rate of progression: he is found at the front most of the time if the group is fast moving and nearer the centre when movement is slow.

In the dense forest environment, every animal in a group was found to be attentive to the movement of the others. On closer examination, Schaller's simple, almost casual, description of this continuous attention may be found to gloss over an essential distinction. For if each gorilla pays attention only to those nearest to itself by keeping them in view, then at times one part of the group might lose sight of the other and they would drift apart. Indeed this would appear likely to happen to the peripheral and especially the visiting males. The dominant male's behaviour, however, suggests that it is designed to demand attention when, for example, by standing motionless, with legs spread, he indicates his readiness to leave a nest area. When he behaves in this way, other members of the group crowd round him. How is the cohesion of the group maintained on other occasions?

If attention is focused on the nearest more dominant animal, a chain of attention would be established within the group, acting as the socially integrating force, each individual being linked to the status class above him by the attention he pays to his immediate superior; attention being finally focused – via the various links – on the dominant male. This form of attention would naturally tend to place the dominant male nearer the front of the group during progression the faster he moves. This fixated attention of subordinate animals would then also be the mechanism by which the dominant male determines the character of group activities. In all essential features this is what happens in a typical baboon or macaque society.

Despite the fact that the frequency of social interactions of all kinds is very low, the most frequent are rank order interactions (0·23 times per hour of observation) and the pattern of this supports an attention structure as outlined. Of 110 such interactions, distributed over the main classes, 51 involved subordinate animals of all classes (half of these, 26, being females) with dominant silver-backed

Plate 1 Dominant male rhesus, *Macaca mulatta* (*centre*), and female consort (*left*). Note sexual swelling displacing hair on the rump

Plate 2 Male Japanese macaque, *Macaca fuscata* (*from Itani*)

Plate 3 (*above*) Male bonnet macaque, *Macaca radiata* (*right*), and consort (*left*) in South India (*from Sugiyama*)

Plate 4 (*left*) Alpha male savannah baboon, *Papio ursinus* – vigilance behaviour (*from Washburn*)

Plate 5 (*top right*) Yellow baboons in the Amboseli Reserve, with warthogs and an impala (*from Washburn*)

Plate 6 (*bottom right*) Gelada, *Theropithecus gelada*, herd at Aostagab, High Semyen. Male harem leader leads his group into centre of the picture. Male in foreground moving aggressively towards right, startling females which look in the direction in which he moves. Babies move to mothers' backs in alarm (*left*). At top of the picture babies sit behind mothers in characteristic position while mother feeds (*from Crook*)

Plate 7 (*top left*) An old (*left*) and young adult male hamadryas baboon, *Papio hamadryas*. Note old male's white cheek-hair (*from Kummer*)

Plate 8 (*bottom left*) A group of hanuman or common langurs, *Presbytis entellus*, in a tree in South India. Large male in the centre, female with young left (*from Sugiyama*)

Plate 9 (*above*) Female patas monkey, *Erythrocebus patas* (*by courtesy of the Zoological Society of London*)

Plate 10 (*right*) Male lar gibbon, *Hylobates lar*, hanging on a narrow branch (*from Ellefson*)

Plate 11 *Gorilla gorilla* male (*by courtesy of Dudley Zoo; photograph by J. E. Rackham*)

Plate 12 (*facing page*) A chimpanzee, *Pan troglodytes*, in Budongo Forest, Uganda (*from Sugiyama*)

Plate 13 A female chimpanzee with a young one on her back wielding a stick at a model leopard in an enclosure (*from Kortlandt*)

Plate 15 A group of female chimpanzees with young, in the Congo (*from Kortlandt*)

males. This interaction suggests that a structure of attention is expressed in the agonistic relations directed towards the dominant silver-backed male, which would tend to hold the group together, and support the conclusions reached by Schaller on the basis of his direct observation: namely, that sub-grouping in the gorilla is a fairly rare phenomenon, occurring usually in groups where more than one silver-backed male is present.

Previous description of gorilla groups suggests that this ape is very different from other primates, yet the evidence here does not support the idea that the way their social integration is achieved differs in any essential way from that of some more distant catarrhine relatives.

The rank-ordered relationships, which include as a central element the relationships between the black-backed and silver-backed males, indicate that the cohort of males is the core of this society; very little other differentiation into sub-groups is evident.

The chimpanzee (Plate 12)

In comparison with the gorilla, the chimpanzee is much more active and much smaller when adult. These are adaptive features which enable it to move about the forest and climb into trees to feed, predominantly on fruit which ripens on the various species of tree, widely spaced in the forest, at different times of the year in different localities. They also live in savannah woodland and their flexed grasp enables them to climb rapidly the tall, branchless paw-paw trees found in these areas.

Two prolonged and careful studies of the chimpanzee in the forest have been made by Vernon and Frankie Reynolds[26] and by Jane Goodall,[27] but the methodological difference of the two approaches has to be understood. A third investigation by Adriaan Kortlandt and his co-worker[28] in both forest and savannah deals with specific abilities in wild and semi-captive chimpanzees and has a special relevance to social organization.

The Reynoldses delineated patterns of association and movement and related these to ecological factors. Jane Goodall lived in much closer proximity to the animals themselves and gives detailed accounts of individual repertoires and types of individuals, but her methods are less appropriate for a wider sociological survey. The patterns of association in a chimpanzee society emerge from the

Reynoldses' study, and we shall, therefore, concentrate attention on their report.

After visiting the various major forests of western Uganda, the Reynoldses chose the Budongo Forest in Bunyoro, which is hilly but not mountainous, with no deep gullies or cliffs to hinder the observers' movements. These were made easier by the tracks already cut through the forest by a sawmill located in the area. The Reynoldses lived in a house overlooking the forest, from which they could locate groups of chimpanzees early in the morning by taking a bearing on their calls and proceeding towards them as far as possible by Jeep along the tracks. Thence they went along animal tracks in the undergrowth to hiding-places below the thick canopy of leaves and creepers close to a group. Often a group could be followed in this way to a new locality, or picked up again the following day at the same spot, especially when it was feeding on the fruit of trees which ripened over a number of days. Details of group movement were obtained in this way, but had to be supplemented by simultaneous observation of more than one group at a time, as the chimpanzees separated and recombined in various ways which, if recorded from individual instances only, would have given a false impression of the predominant groupings and movements of groups. This became easier once the factors governing the movements of the chimpanzees were understood; for example, the ripening of fruit was found to play an important part. The movement of groups could then, to some extent, be anticipated, and individual groups watched as they crossed the tracks. This was done by enlisting a number of local men for a three-week period. They stationed themselves at the track intersections during the period of maximum movement – for three hours after dawn and from 4 to 7 p.m. A method was devised for the recognition of individuals and their companions, and this could be combined with simultaneous checks on their whereabouts and interactions. Within nine months this yielded a surprisingly suggestive picture.

The Reynoldses found that any one fruit tree is visited regularly only by some groups of individuals, which they called bands. For example:

> ... A white-backed old male and a white-backed female fed on
> the tree on five of the eight observation days. The black haired

males and one grey-backed male were also frequent visitors in the mornings, but usually left after an hour's feeding. Six other females, three with juveniles, fed on the tree on one or more days. The times of arrival and departure from the tree varied with the individual, and never did all the animals arrive or leave as a group. Once there was three hours' difference between the departure time of the first and last individual. Four times one chimpanzee remained behind alone in the tree for as long as two hours, twice a mother with her juveniles and twice the old male.

A patch of Anigeria trees observed for twenty-six consecutive days was included in the daily round of a number of bands of different composition on most of the days. From observations made in this way an individual or small band could be recognized and a note made of the many different individuals associated with it. This method of observation shows that the chimpanzees do not form *closed* heterosexual groups, for the groups seen at any one locality had a constantly changing membership and composition, 'splitting apart, meeting others and joining, congregating and dispersing'.

It would be easy to conclude from these facts that the organization of the social structure had very little in common with that of the gorilla or the baboon, for example. Supplemented, however, by the method of observing chimpanzees as they crossed the paths in the forest, the consistency and composition of the bands becomes a more obvious feature.

The frequent types of composition were: (1) adult bands, containing adults of both sexes, and occasionally adolescents, but not including any mothers with dependent young; (2) male bands, containing only adult males; (3) mother bands, containing only mothers with young, and, occasionally, other females; (4) mixed bands, containing mothers with young, other females, adolescents and adult males.

The first three simple subdivisions are the same as the main subdivisions of larger groups which have been distinguished in the societies of the Japanese and Indian macaque, where they remain within a cohesive group. The consistent appearance of bands of the same adult males is, however, specially noteworthy. For example, one small band of four adult males was seen on eight separate days from late June to mid-October, and seemed to be a relatively stable unit, associating sometimes with other members of the population.

> This band of four males was seen several times, feeding together in Maesopsis trees, apart from the other bands, which would be up to half a mile away. Several times they were seen together with large aggregations, including mothers, juveniles and other adults, or they would be joined by one or two adults or oestrus females who would depart before any of the others, the males of a group leaving a site where they had been grooming or feeding within minutes of each other. On frequent occasions they were seen in company with each other, crossing the tracks which went through the forest.

The Reynoldses' assessment of all their data revealed that out of the travelling bands, those composed of adult males or adult males and childless adult females were seen most frequently – twice as often as any other type of band – and he concludes that bands containing adult males travel farther than the others in search of fruiting trees. The rest of the less mobile population is made aware of newly-ripened fruit by the calls and drummings of these more mobile bands. The uneven distribution of fruiting trees and the difference in mobility between the more sedentary mothers with young and others of a population leads to the varying association between bands and free moving individuals.

> Almost always when mother bands were seen travelling they were part of a large scale movement of many groups to a new focus of activity, whereas adults often moved to and fro between such areas, independently of other group movements.

In this way the population is concentrated to exploit the food supply.

Thus while it is evident that, as the Reynoldses put it, chimpanzees have a wider compass of social inter-relationships than do most other primates studied in the wild (and he has provided reasons for regarding this as an adjustment to their feeding habits), it seems equally clear that Kortlandt's assertion that individual participation in dif-

108

ferent kinds of aggregations is not fixed or controlled in any way is not borne out by the Reynoldses more comprehensive study. Indeed, if the question be asked whether or not the bands represent the same grouping tendencies found in the gorilla, baboon or macaque, then the answer would appear to be yes. As bands of adult males of fixed composition are a distinct part of the population, these represent the core element present, but temporarily detached from the rest of the population. Unfortunately, no data on the nature of the relations of these males could be obtained by the Reynoldses' method, and Goodall did not have sufficient data to assess the type of band within which she was working at close quarters.

In a comparative study which was made by Itani and Suzuki[29] in the savannah woodland of western Tanzania in October 1965, they encountered a group of wild chimpanzees consisting of 43 individuals, and recorded its mode of progression. This fell into three parts; the first consisted of 21 females and infants (8 of the females were mothers with infants), the second central part were all adult males (7), and the third part consisted of 11 females (5 of which were in oestrus) and 4 young, so that in the savannah woodland this group contained a cohort of males, but after entering a riverine forest they regrouped themselves into heterogeneous groups. Some of the adult males left the cohort and formed heterosexual groups with females and young.

We maintain that they have demonstrated that the population contains the central features or homologues of the rank order between adult males which are found in the more rigid societies of baboons and macaques and by so doing have shown that increased flexibility has been introduced into a social structure which the chimpanzee holds in common with these other primates, but in a way different from the gorilla. At least this hypothesis should serve to direct future observations towards devising methods for obtaining the essential information that may substantiate this interpretation.

Features of agonistic interaction

Individual behaviour in agonistic relations, of which three-quarters takes place between adult males and only 8 per cent between adult females, is described by Goodall for the individuals with which she was closely associated.

When two chimpanzees meet, or even when they are in competition for the same piece of food, one will give way or – ' . . . the subordinate chimpanzee may make a detour, or may approach the other and either present or reach out to touch the dominant animal on the lips, thighs, or genital area'. These incidents were rare, and even rarer the occasions when one chimpanzee ran off screaming from another 'excited or angry chimpanzee'.

Of the 'tame' males in the group Goodall frequented, two old males (A and B) appeared to be equals except when a third (and very dominant) male was present, when one of them (A) dominated the other (B) because, as she says, of 'the greater degree of agonistic attraction between A and the very dominant male'.

In the agonistic behaviour described by the Reynoldses, sudden attacks by slapping, pushing and running at the companion were frequently combined with mutual hand-touching.

Both observers are therefore describing the close association of agonistic behaviour with various forms of apparent reassurance obtained through contact. The quick alternation between contact and agonistic behaviour, part of which it should be noted itself involves contact, is the peculiar characteristic of a chimpanzee, and the same feature is evident in Kortlandt's description of the association between members of a group during agonistic social displays and during the harassing of large predators.

Kortlandt and his collaborator, working with forest-dwelling chimpanzees in the Beni reserve in Kivu province of the Congo, (both wild and in large enclosures) and with savannah-dwelling and forest chimpanzees of eastern Guinea, have been able to demonstrate that the communal displays noted also by the Reynoldses in which members of a group go around leaping about, shaking saplings and young trees, breaking off branches and shouting in chorus, take on a directed and much more definite form as group harassing displays and during attacks on a model leopard.

In these studies the stuffed leopard was pulled out of a hide in the presence of a band of chimpanzees, and their subsequent behaviour was observed and filmed. Following a moment of dead silence on catching sight of the leopard, there was a burst of yelling and barking, accompanied by every member of the group charging about in a different direction. A few fled, but returned soon afterwards to join the majority, who began leaping up and down and charging the leopard, brandishing big sticks or broken-off trees, throwing these 'weapons' in the direction of the 'predator', all the while beating the ground and stamping on it with hands and feet.

At the end of a charge they would frequently lash out with flexible trees still rooted to the ground, but often from a very short distance so that these would hit the leopard. Many of the charges in which brandishing, throwing and swishing of sticks took place were performed bipedally. Some of the bloodcurdling barking was loud enough to wake a human neighbour six hundred metres away. Interspersed with these communal or individual charges were periods of silence and stillness which were followed by periods of seeking and giving reassurance by holding out the hands to be kissed, touching of their neighbours and homo and hetero pseudo-copulations. Voiding of diarrhoea and enormous amounts of intense body scratching took place.

The attacks on the leopard were more or less rhythmical, and followed by brief increases in fear symptoms and the seeking of reassurance and longer periods of sitting down watching the leopard (when some chimpanzees would start eating). The aggressive aspects gradually waned after about half an hour, being replaced by intense inquisitiveness. One chimpanzee poked it with its fist, another smelt at it and finally, in one of the episodes with the savannah chimpanzees, the leopard's head was detached from the body and rolled about. Another chimpanzee seized the tail and they all rushed off into the bush with its body.

The following points are characteristic of these displays. Although the patterns of intimidation behaviour and agonistic tool-use are very varied, they are nearly always aimed straight at the leopard, in striking contrast to similar behaviour in social intercourse, where it is rarely aimed at anyone. This aim is from a segment of a circle of some 200° around the head end of the leopard (see Plate 13). The agonistic tool-use consists of brandishing a stick sideways, up and down, and, in the case of the forest chimpanzees, the tools are thrown a ridiculously short distance.

The considerable differences in the various forms of harassment or intimidation displays towards the model leopard are, according to Kortlandt, related to whether or not the chimpanzees live in the forest or the savannah. A chimpanzee group caught from savannah in the Congo and a group of savannah-living chimpanzees from eastern Guinea both showed the following features when confined with the model leopard in a large enclosure:

1. Clubs, made from defoliated branches 1 to 2 metres in length, were most often used while walking, one end being held in the hand and the other being pointed and swung up and down in the direction of the leopard, effectively enough to direct furious blows in several instances, in a way homologous to human fighting with clubs (unlike the uprooted branches still with leaves on used by the forest chimpanzees, which are more effective intimidation 'tools').
2. In throwing the aim was nearly always perfect, contrary to all instances seen in forest-dwelling chimpanzees, which had poor aim and often dropped the stick a short distance from the hand.
3. All locomotion was much more frequently bipedal than that of the forest dwellers.
4. Simultaneous assaults by the assailants and vocal support by the onlookers amounted to tactical co-ordination of the group during the advance on the leopard.

From these differences between forest and savannah dwellers it can be seen that the forest chimpanzee intimidation displays are more erratic and are therefore better adapted to driving off the predator in a forest. Open savannah, on the other hand, requires concerted attacks to achieve the same result.

Kortlandt and Kooij point out that

no reliable observer known to me has ever seen savannah-dwelling chimpanzees walking around with any kind of weapon in their hands, in spite of the fact that they sometimes walk for miles through entirely open country, even in predator-crowded areas. All this indicates that, for adult chimpanzees at least, the risk of being killed by a leopard, hyaena or lion is virtually non-existent.

Kortlandt noted that a model leopard with a model baby chimpanzee as victim induced much more vigorous attack, both in savannah and forest chimpanzees; mothers with young were more aggressive towards the model with or without a victim. It would appear that this is a co-operative effort in defence of the young which could be effective in saving the lives of infants if, by harassing, leopards are cleared from the district or can be induced to release their prey. Jane Goodall has noted that the young often wander away from their mothers, but are always kept in sight and usually within reach.

CHAPTER FOUR

Growing up in Society

MOTHER AND YOUNG

The behaviour of the young primate of both arboreal species and species that live on the ground reflects the habits of its arboreal ancestors. Whereas other mammals, such as rodents, deposit their young in a nest where they remain for several days and are periodically visited by the mother, or else are able to run and follow their mother within a few hours of birth (as are the young ungulates living in open plains), the young of most subhuman primates show one predominant pattern of behaviour: they cling to their mothers' fur. By this means, and (to varying extents in different species) assisted by the mother to cling on to her body, the infant monkey or ape is carried large distances over open or mountainous country or through arboreal pathways.

Important studies of the mother/infant relationships have been made by the Harlows[1] on captive rhesus monkeys, by Jay[2] and Sugiyama[3] on wild langurs, and by Hall and DeVore[4] on the society of the savannah baboon, and the phases of the mother/infant relationship have been discovered. Three factors contribute to the social development of the young. They are:

1. The processes of maturation in the infant, which include not only maturation of physical ability and skill but also concomitant changes in its behaviour.
2. Changes of behaviour of the mother.
3. The amount and diversity of social relationships which the infant experiences.

These three factors differ greatly from species to species. Hinde and Spencer-Booth[5] have shown that the mother/infant relationship in rhesus monkeys is greatly influenced by the amount of contact with other social companions. These contacts may start at the moment of birth or appear only later, when the infant moves out into society.

The mammalian species which move in open country rely little on circumscribed regions for refuge and more on the cohesion of the group as a whole. The less mature animals seek the protection of more adult individuals. Mother is a haven, a refuge and a fixed point of orientation for all early independent movement, except among some prosimians. The following combination of factors applies with greater intensity to the behaviour of the young primate than to any other mammalian group: the young monkey or ape escapes to mother rather than returning to the nest, and the subsequent freedom of movement for the infant is as much dependent on ability to integrate into the society as to move over the ground and to cope with physical obstacles. This is true of all species of primates and is the reason for giving special consideration to the mother/infant relationship, which is a universal relationship throughout the primates, constituting a stem structure in the societies of sub-human primates surpassing in cohesiveness even that of the male cohorts.

Rhesus mother and young

When the infant rhesus is born, its behaviour seems to be made up of a number of entirely separate reflexes. Touching of the cheeks or the lips, for example, will cause a turning of the head in that direction, and then an opening of the mouth and clasping parts of the fur or the nipple with the lips or jaws. Baboon and langur infants as well as the rhesus infant use this jaw-hold as a means of support. Sucking is a separate response. Placed face down on an open surface the infant will turn itself on its back. If the plantar surface of a hand or foot is stimulated it will grasp whatever is in reach so that (combined with the tensing of the limbs) the animal is able to hold itself on to the mother's fur. All these, it may be noted, are *contact* reflexes. Within a few days, however, the infant begins to notice other animals around it, to recognize the face of its mother and to reach out for support, making feeble attempts to move about. By the tenth day this process is nearly complete, though the persistent weakness of the hind legs is associated with the fact that the hind feet are still controlled by these plantar reflexes, whereas the front end of the body has already come under the control of more distant awareness.

The first stage of post-natal attachment to and protection by the mother starts at birth. Soon after birth the infant begins to cling to the ventral surface of the mother's body, while the mother responds by clasping it to her body and cradling it in her arms or, while sitting, in the groin. While the baby is in this position it frequently holds the nipple in its mouth, but does not always suck. Immediately after birth the mother's movements are fairly restricted, and during this time Siddiqi[6] reports that the infant alternates between periods of half an hour asleep and a quarter to half an hour active nursing. During the first thirty to forty days of its life the infant increases the extent of its excursions away from the mother and the frequency of her retrieving and restraining activity also increases. When the baby tries to move away she catches hold of its tail and holds on for long periods of time. During this phase of retrieving by the mother she grooms the infant more, but at the end of this phase grooming, retrieving and protecting activities fall off sharply, and the mother contents herself with keeping her infant under observation.

In the rhesus monkey studied by Harlow,[7] two forms of retrieving at a distance were observed whenever mother and infant were disturbed by some event. One was a type of grin directed at the infant by the mother which brought the young one back to her; the other was a form of posturing comparable to the sexual presentation pattern of the female. This involved movement of the mother towards the infant and was more effective in bringing about its return.

The status of the rhesus mother does not change in any way after the birth of her child, and whenever she is approached by any member of the troop she retreats with her infant; therefore she remains as before, somewhat isolated as an individual.

Growing up in a langur society

Within a few hours of birth the infant langur can, unaided, cling to its mother so tightly that she is able to run or make long jumps without dislodging it. The mother inspects, licks, grooms and manipulates the infant from the hour of its birth, and is immediately surrounded by clusters of other mothers and females who gently reach out to touch, lick and smell the newborn infant. For at least a few hours after birth the mother usually turns her back on the waiting females, and only when the infant is dry does she allow them to handle it. During these early hours while it rests quietly, she grooms and strokes it softly without disturbing or even waking it. As soon as it is dry she allows another female to take it in her arms and hold it, and the infant is then closely inspected and gently manipulated, nudged, licked and smelt by this other female. Special attention is given to inspecting the infant's head, hands and genitals. At the first sign of discomfort in the newborn it will be taken by another of the waiting females, if not by its mother. However, she is able to take it back from any of the females, regardless of their status.

There exists an enormous individual variation among females in the way they handle an infant. Some hold it at a distance, while others allow it to cling close and even assist it. Some allow it to take the nipple in its mouth while it is pressed against their chest, and others will prevent it from doing this. Some are adept at holding it, and it will rest happily with them for long periods of time, while others are not, and it will soon squeal when in their care. A tense, nervous and easily-irritated female may frequently startle the infant with quick unpredictable motions, while a calm and more relaxed one makes few sudden movements. Jay reports that multiparous females are better mothers than primiparous ones and says that nulliparous, subadult and young females show more awkwardness in handling the young than the older ones, who seem to have gained experience.

The infant is the centre of interest of all mothers and females of a langur group. Because it is frequently passed round from female to female, it is subjected to the care of every type of female in such a group. All infants are therefore likely to have the same or similar handling during their early life and not to have different experiences because of the status of their mother. The ultimate effects of this unique process on the socialization of the langur infant would be an interesting subject for study. It is of great importance that when the infant needs help in steadying itself or in clinging, it grasps its mother's fur and touches her. She then immediately supports it. Shifting position, clinging or falling appear to stimulate her so that she holds, adjusts and finally fondles the infant. Adult males take no interest in the young and play no part in their protection. A mother with an infant is rarely seen within fifteen feet of an adult male, and the latter may be threatened or chased off by the mother.

A touch by the mother's hand or, should the infant be at a distance, a sweeping gesture of her arm indicates to the youngster that she is about to move off and it clings to her. At this stage an infant does not appear to be relaxed unless in contact with the mother's body. A contented infant is usually silent, but whenever seriously disturbed – sometimes even when the mother holds it out for inspection – it emits sounds of rising intensity up to loud squeals. The mother immediately responds by grooming it.

Within two weeks an infant which is being held by another female can recognize its mother from a distance of twenty feet and, unless restrained by the female grasping it, may make a few hesitant attempts to reach her, but it takes a month before the infant is able to move up to half a dozen feet on its own. At this stage, when the infant begins to move away from its mother, its coat colour, quality of movement, vocalization and its size appear to be factors which release maternal attention. No adult was seen to threaten an infant.

The infant supplements its milk diet with solid food at about three months and follows the mother about, learning her food habits. At five months it begins to change its brown colour, becoming lighter, and by then it will often be left by its mother with another mother and her own infant, so that one female may sit with several young at once. Although still tolerant towards it, the mother's active interest in the infant begins to decline. She still protects it and is constantly aware of its whereabouts, and when the group is alerted she will call it to her. When the infant has reached the age of six months it will spend much of its time at a considerable distance from its mother, but by then mother and infant will call to one another. Several hours of the infant's day will now be spent at play with its companions. The average size of a play group is only two to four, but it may contain as many as sixteen. Vigorous activities such as running, jumping, chasing, wrestling and tail-pulling are supplemented by more complicated forms of play (oriented towards aspects of the physical environment and any objects that may be moved about). All play is basically social and exploratory.

By eight months the males become larger and stronger and the play groups split into groups of equally sized animals. Squeals and grunts can be heard during play, but no loud crying; indeed any loud noises result in interference from adults. Dominance and sex behaviour appear. Differences between the behaviour of the males and of the females begin to show, although Sugiyama reports the appearance of this difference much later – at twenty months.

Adult females act as mothers and protectors to the young of both sexes. As a ten-month-old female has no contact with males she does not require to take initiative at this time to relate herself to the adult male. The infant male of ten months, on the other hand, now begins to relate himself to adult males by a unique form of approach. He runs to the moving adult in a highly specialized manner, squealing tensely, but veers away just before touching him. About a week later the infant male approaches and mounts an adult male by pulling himself up over the adult's hindquarters. In a few weeks another element is added when the infant runs round to face and embrace the adult male. Touching, mounting and embracing occur thereafter either as a series or as separate events. An adult may be mounted and embraced by as many as four infant and juvenile males in rapid succession, and this behaviour continues to be shown by juveniles until they are approximately four years old. The adult male sometimes plays in the juvenile group. In contrast, the female infant has no contact with adult males. Instead, she spends more time grooming and being groomed by adult females than does the male infant. The older infant also participates in grooming activities with other infant or juvenile females.

By about one year of age infants of both sexes join in alerting the group by alarm calls. From the eleventh to the fifteenth month the infant is weaned from the mother. This is a distinctive, apparently agonistic period in the mother/infant relationship.

During weaning the mother becomes more and more hostile and denying. At first she simply avoids the infant, moving away from it and taking long jumps from tree to tree, making it difficult for the infant to follow. When it manages to catch up with her she merely turns away, but if the infant persists in trying to be nursed she pushes it off with outstretched arms. The infant may then squeal and jerk and become tense. It crouches and glares in her face and runs round to stay in front of her when she turns away. The mother's agonistic behaviour towards the infant may alternate occasionally with allowing it to cling.

After several months the mother may well ignore the infant's persistence for as long as thirty minutes, and even the most boisterous tantrum seldom draws her attention, or that of other adults. If other females are disturbed by this behaviour they either move away or threaten the mother, but she does not return the threat. Some mothers even mock-bite their infants during the period of rejection until their sexual cycles return, when they drive the infant off completely. As the mother's rejection activities mount they become more and more agonistic and strenuous for her. In its final attempt to retain her, the infant strikes her and screams as it jumps about her, shaking the branches near her. When the infant has reached the age of about fourteen months this type of behaviour elicits threats from other members of the adult community, particularly towards male infants, which are the more active.

Mother and young in a savannah baboon society

The relationship of the infant rhesus to its mother during the first month is almost identical with that of the langur. The infant baboon, however, gets more grooming interspersed with lipsmacking and licking. These seem to be gestures of pacification, compensating for the fact that when the infant is not sucking the mother constantly turns it about and inspects it so that it is not able to take the nipple for more than a few minutes at a time. Whenever the baboon mother starts to move she grasps her infant to her with one hand for a few moments and then it clings on by itself for the rest of the time she is in motion, but she will clasp it to her when she comes to rest, which gives it some relaxation after hanging on. Baboons move up to three times as far as langurs in their daily travels, and if at any point the infant fails to maintain its position it begins to drag its feet on the ground. The baboon mother then stops and sits down with her infant for a short while, or holds it close to her while she gallops after the troop.

In the baboon society a female which is in anoestrus has little contact with the males, and during pregnancy the situation is much the same, but as soon as her infant is born she becomes a centre of interest for the troop. Because dominant males are interested she moves with her baby to the heart of the troop where the central hierarchy males are, and her status rises accordingly. Thereby she becomes immune from threats by other members of the troop. The dominant males take an interest in all infants of the troop, of which there may be as many as twenty in a troop of two hundred by the end of the season of births in December, so that a situation arises similar to that in the Japanese macaque in which a rank order of males is surrounded by females with young, and these in turn are surrounded by the younger, less dominant males at the edge of the troop. All members of a baboon troop, except young infants, attempt to groom the mother and afterwards touch the infant. Apart from the dominant male, only the older juveniles and the females are permitted to do this by the dominant males. Younger juveniles and older infants are driven away. The mother, however, tolerates the interest in her infant very uneasily and never lets the infant leave her arms.

Approaching females, now subordinate in status, may be required to drop their hindquarters in a form of appeasing presentation before being accepted by the mother. A young female, who may have been successful in starting the grooming, is soon replaced by a more dominant female, and previously dominant females now approach the mother with suitable submission gestures. In contrast, the approach of the adult males is direct and straightforward and the mother cringes, showing her relative subordination, even while she is accepted in the presence of the dominant males. Their approaches are often accompanied by vigorous lipsmacking as a form of reassurance. The degree of interest taken by these dominant males varies very much from member to member: some even carry the young on their bellies for as long as twenty minutes. All members of a troop are aware of distress cries of infants and attack whoever it may be that is close to an infant in distress.

Rank order relations in the baboon society are very marked and agonistic encounters intense, and the aggregation of members round a mother is also accompanied by a large amount of grooming. In this area large grooming parties and clusters develop. The interest in infants evidently creates a bond not only between the mother and other females but between adult males and the mother, and by bringing so many individuals close together causes a large amount of grooming to take place between them.

121

From the fourth to the sixth month the young baboon rides jockey style on the mother's back (see Plate 14), close to the tail, though it lies flat when the mother runs. Occasionally it touches or chews foods which the mother herself eats. It constantly explores the physical environment up to a distance of twenty yards away from the mother, and begins to play with other infants. Both these activities increase steadily over the next six months.

Ambivalence in the mother/infant relationship

In the langur society the weaning period is the period of most evident ambivalence in the mother/child relationship, but other studies have shown that such ambivalence is present from birth. In the first phase of the infant's life, when it clings to the mother or is cradled in her arms, its behaviour consists entirely of separate reflexes. Its movements contain no directed component which would enable it to return to its mother and any spontaneous movement is restrained by her holding on to the infant and clutching it close to her. As soon as the infant strays and is able to return to her it may meet with momentary rejection by the mother, and the frequency with which this occurs increases gradually as it grows older. Hence the mother's relationship to the infant always contains an element of ambivalence which changes its characteristics, dependent on the infant's behaviour. In the first phase this ambivalence arises because of the mother's restraining action, and during the second and longer phase it is replaced by her occasional rejection of the infant's approaches.

In small groups of caged rhesus monkeys, what are described as tantrums or bursts of violent jerking of the body, accompanied by screaming and a kind of stuttering call, follow rejection by the mother and reach a maximum frequency during the nineteenth to twenty-fourth weeks. More often than not the mother will be provoked to collect the infant. Infants mothered on surrogates show a much higher frequency of jerking, cooing and screeching than do those which are cared for by their own mothers. This suggests that the 'tantrum' is not caused by the mother's rejection but by the absence of adequate mothering, or, during periods when the infant is rejected, by inadequate provision of gratification while in contact with the mother.

Status of the mother

Imanishi[9] points out that the infants of dominant females at the centre of the troop of the Japanese macaques apparently learn from the adults around them a domineering attitude towards peripheral troop members. They are more likely to adopt roles of leadership in adult life. A similar observation by DeVore[10] is made of the effects of the mother's status on her infant and her relationship to the infant in baboon society. He noticed that infants whose mothers were near the bottom of the hierarchy gave alarm cries more often and made more frequent demands; that is to say these infants persistently demanded nursing and tried to ride their mother's backs many weeks after their companions had ceased doing either. This suggests that some of the factors we have already discussed which bring about an excessive attachment of the infant to the mother have been operative in the behaviour of these low-ranking mothers. Such mothers, because they are the subject of attack by more dominant mothers, are less responsive to their infants and may be prevented from giving them adequate nursing. In addition, because low-ranking mothers get involved in disputes more often, their infants are subjected more frequently to periods of agonistic behaviour. A low-ranking female, continually subjected to dominance by others, suffers 'emotional upsets' which are detected by the infant and cause it to run back to her.

In baboon society low-ranking mothers are excitable, easily startled and jerky in the way they handle their infants; similar excitable behaviour may reflect low rank in langur society also. However, Jay suggests that, as there is no noticeable rank order between langur mothers, the factor most affecting the infant is whether the mother is excitable or relaxed.

By contrast, infants of dominant baboon mothers are less involved in agonistic encounters and show a greater freedom of movement. In these infants there is no intensification of the clinging response which is shown by the infants of subordinate mothers.

To sum up, one may surmise that infants of more dominant females tend to be more 'secure', to have greater freedom of movement, to have less dependence on their mothers and to have more varied and greater experience. Thus they build up a greater repertoire of behaviour by a given age than the infants of lower-ranking females. We would expect that, if their mother were lost, the off-spring of a dominant female would be freer in approach to other females and would have a greater variety of behaviour for coping with the situation, so that such an experience would disrupt them less.

From their experience of isolated youngsters, Kaufman and Rosenblum[11] argue that offspring of submissive females would not so freely approach other females and by comparison would have an impoverished repertoire of coping behaviour. The experience of losing the mother might be overwhelming for them, although, as pointed out earlier, this expectation makes no allowance for the possible compensating behaviour of other members of the society.

In monkeys the likelihood of a previous attraction between a young infant and an adult other than the mother depends in large part on the hierarchical status relationships between the infant's mother and the other animal. In general the evidence seems to be that an infant is more likely to have had a positive relationship with the females of the same or lower status than its mother. Hinde and Spencer-Booth reported that the rhesus mothers allowed subordin-ate females to carry and cuddle their infants, and this was especially true if the other female had been their usual sitting and grooming companion. On the other hand, advances to an infant, whether aggressive or otherwise, by a more dominant female were likely to produce protective behaviour by the mother, including termination of an infant's interaction with the 'aunt'. They also reported that adult females would at times show aggressive behaviour to infants not their own and this was greater if they were dominant animals or if they had infants of their own.

There are at least two components involved in successful turning to a substitute. The first is the effort by the infant to do so, and the second is the nature of the adult's responses. Both of these are likely to be modified by previous experience. An adoption cited by Hinde and Spencer-Booth (the other reports offer no data on this matter) was made by an adult which had a previous positive relationship to the infant and its mother. This would suggest then that an adult which had previously had a close relationship with an infant and its mother would be more likely to respond positively to an infant's appeal for care.

In Japanese macaque society a mother's high status places her and her infant in the breeding hierarchy at the centre of the society. The females with which contacts are made will all share her high status. Status within the female assemblies is therefore important in the way that the young are established in society, and gives them what is called a dependent status – namely, that of their mothers. In those societies where the females do not participate much or for long in the juvenile clusters, their dependent status is a major influence in their later life, but all males ultimately derive their adult status from their experience in the juvenile clusters and their prowess in maintaining status in the male cohorts.

The importance of the mother/young relationship is also emphasized by observations made by Walter Angst[12] on a long-established colony of *Macaca fascicularis* in the Basel Zoo. He finds that whenever a mother or one of her offspring are involved in agonistic encounters with others, the rest of the maternal group comes to the assistance of the threatened member.

Male care of infants

A type of behaviour which crops up occasionally in *Papio cynocephalus* society and plays a central part in the organization of hamadryas baboon society is the male care of infants. It is also a notable feature of the behaviour of some males in certain Japanese macaque groups during the season when the infants are born. It is probably an extension of the interest typical of baboon and macaque societies which adults of both sexes (particularly males) take in infants. Nevertheless, it is in marked contrast to the behaviour of most primate males, for they usually avoid infants – as do some of the adult females. Itani,[13] who made this study on the Japanese macaque, points out that the male care of the infant is similar to the behaviour of a mother towards her infant, apart from the absence of suckling.

Japanese macaques in captivity quite often snatch up babies and hold them when approached by a keeper, and let them go as soon as the keeper leaves the enclosure, and some adult males establish a close relationship with an infant. In one pastured troop a female died, leaving a six-month-old male baby, which immediately took shelter under a sub-leader. This adult male showed no inclination to hug it, but he always walked with it and groomed it carefully.

This relationship lasted for six months. Of special interest is the adult male who had as a grooming partner a female with an infant. When the male baby was seventy-three days old it was seen running after the adult male, the mother calling after it, but she ceased calling it when it jumped into the arms of and was held by the adult male. As infants grow up, they are more and more tolerated in the neighbourhood of adults. Play groups may be active in their vicinity, and when an adult male is attacked by the young in play there is no retaliation.

What Itani terms 'paternal' care occurs when a large number of centrally placed adult males of the breeding hierarchy each start cradling a particular infant during the birth season. This behaviour is directed towards the one- and two-year-old infants of both sexes, though in one year twenty out of twenty-five infants cared for by males were females. Sometimes the relationship established between the adult male and the infant in his care persists or may reappear the following year. In the Japanese macaque society adult males are divided into the leader class, which is in the centre (consisting in this instance of six males), the sub-leader class of ten males, and a third class of males in the outer portion of the troop. This last class was further subdivided into three sub-sections, depending on age. The protector males, as those caring for infants were called, belonged either to the leader class, the sub-leader class or the first sub-class of the peripheral males. Hence it was found that an infant of a female occupying the central part of the group was more likely to receive 'paternal' care than one living on the periphery.

The individual characteristics of the behaviour of adult males showing 'paternal' care were analysed into social, aggressive and centre-seeking traits of behaviour (centre-seeking = showing an interest in being in the centre of the group). Itani found that, excluding the highly aggressive dominant members of the leader class, in general the higher his sociability and interest in the central part of the group the more an individual is likely to show 'paternal' care, provided these two are combined with a low degree of aggressiveness. Further analysis showed that individuals whose social position was least stable showed 'paternal' care more frequently. Itani suggests that they are tolerated near to the supremely dominant male by virtue of the similarity of their behaviour to that of females with their infants. At least one instance was seen of a sub-leader moving into the central part successfully while hugging an infant.

Since we already know that two- to four-year-old females show a strong interest in babies and fondle them, this male care supplements female care in some societies and shows that to the extent that the young always establish social bonds with other members of the community, the death of the mother does not deprive the young of care. Therefore studies of the young in isolation are unnatural.*

The life of the juvenile and subadult

The langur

Once the young langur has severed its ties with the mother, much of its time is spent in groups with other young, playing and foraging together. Its relationship to adults becomes more like that of adults to each other. At this stage, however, differences in the behaviour of juvenile langurs become evident between male and female. Dominance interactions occur more frequently, but less among female juveniles than among the males. The females spend less time playing during the day, usually with other female juveniles and infants. As the juveniles grow up, so their play becomes restricted more and more to their own sex.

---

* *Artificial Separation.* Kaufman's study[14] of the pigtail macaque (*Macaca nemestrina*) infants separated from their mothers confirms that this separation increases the vigour with which both the young and the mother re-establish contact and maintain contact for longer periods after they have been reunited. A similar process can be seen in the case of those infants whose mothers frequently reject them. But a difference exists here, for whereas the attention of the rejected infant is directed to the mother and the infant's behaviour maintains this orientation towards her in later life when it has learned to keep its distance (thus forming a basis for attachment when adult), after artificial separation an infant clings longer and later into life.

Kaufman also shows that separation produces a state of depression, during which exploratory behaviour is reduced or eliminated, leaving only the survival responses of a quick response to aggressive behaviour and rapid and often voracious response to the offer of food. Contrary to Kaufman's views, this condition, in which the responses enhancing growth of the infant's repertoire are eliminated, does not help the individual to survive, as in a primate social environment there is a survival premium, if not a total reliance for survival, on socialization processes. The apparent contradiction arises here from the extreme nature of the laboratory isolate, which presupposes that such a situation would arise in the wild without compensating changes occurring in the behaviour of other members of the society such as adoption by another adult, or friendship with a juvenile. Nevertheless, the evidence helps to define behavioural changes in the infant, which do occur frequently at a much lower intensity. We shall see that Kaufman's studies may have a bearing on the way the mother's status affects the infant.

By ten months the female infant has begun to groom, mainly in female groups. This is before weaning. Grooming is the main form of social behaviour between female juveniles and adult females. Male juveniles seldom initiate grooming, unless it is to placate adults or get closer to food. Subadult females, on the other hand, groom adult females frequently. Subadult males generally remain peripheral to the group and do not have contact with adults, especially with females, except when they are relaxed and come together for grooming. Subadult females, on the other hand, have wide-ranging social contacts, though they are mostly oriented to females in the female group. At this stage the young female behaves both aggressively and with submission to adult males who may threaten her, but she does not groom them. Male juveniles increase their typical approaches to adult males. On the other hand, the adult male, having only slight agonistic relationships with the adult female, can participate in strong grooming relationships with her. It is tempting to suggest (see Chapter 5) that the relationship between the adult males and the subadult males is that form which develops at a higher level of arousal, whereas the grooming relationships (which bind the adult males to the females and many of the juvenile females to other females as well as juvenile males to females) are of a lower order of arousal and constitute the basis of a different kind of bond.

Subordinate to all adult males, the subadult male never disputes his lower position, unlike the baboon male. During fights and threatening he stays at a safe distance. If threatened by an adult male which does not continue to threaten him, he will run up to and touch, and occasionally embrace this adult male; but mounting being a gesture of dominance, he no longer includes this in the repertoire of approach as he did when a juvenile. There is often tension when subadult males and adult females are near each other, unless the group is very relaxed. The tension may cause fighting.

If an adult female is threatened by a more dominant adult, she may turn and threaten a small subadult male instead of the more dominant animal. This re-directed aggression also initiates fights, involving both subadult males and adult females. That females have no means of coping with high agonistic relationships is shown by the fact that an adult female, together with her infants and juveniles, will move away from males when they fight amongst themselves or

128

with subadult males. This is, however, a relatively infrequent occurrence.

It is possible to see very clearly in this description the separation of the females into their groups, with bonds based on grooming relationships, and also the appearance of several stages of the agonistic bond between males, based on their peculiar form of behaviour.

The young savannah baboon

By the end of the first year the young animal is no longer nursing, but remains close to the mother and feeds with her. She is tolerant of it being close to her, but allows it to wander away from her. The males also remain completely tolerant of the young animal's presence. Females other than the mother may, however, occasionally threaten and even attack a young animal, holding it down or giving it a token bite. The screeching young may then elicit a counter-attack from the mother or from an adult male.

The process of weaning the young continues over its second year, during which time it is increasingly rejected by the mother when trying to take the nipple or ride her back, and its own behaviour towards her increasingly takes the form of grooming. When the mother comes back into sexual activity and her privileged status with the males is lost, the young one has become a juvenile. It no longer feeds with the mother, but plays and feeds with its age mates. Now, when in danger, it flees to the adult males. The fact that adult males tolerate play around them at all stages in the youngster's development, while females – other than the mother – tend to reject them more and more as they grow up must influence the selection of animals to whom to run when fleeing in adult life.

A contradiction may appear to be present in this description of the way the young male reacts to threats from females on the one hand and males on the other, but there is probably a major difference between the threats it receives from the females (which ward off the young by virtue of persistent threats) whereas the males are probably only intermittently threatening youngsters, since they tolerate their presence near by. The fluctuating arousal thereby brought about in the young male leads to withdrawal followed by approach in a way discussed more fully in Chapter 6.

The older juvenile completes the transition to an independent young adult in its third and fourth year. During the early part of this period it is still oriented towards its own age group, but as dominance interactions become more intense in the behaviour of the juveniles towards each other, so the adult males cease to tolerate the play by these juveniles. Instead they threaten them, particularly when they are rough with infants or younger juveniles. At this stage the paths of the sexes separate: the females leave the juvenile play group and join the grooming assemblies of adult females. By the end of this period a female is sexually fully mature and becomes an adult.

As the full muscular and skeletal growth, the complete eruption of the canine teeth and the development of the shoulder mantle may take as long as eight years, the males remain in a subadult condition for the next four years. During this interval males become larger than females and by the end of the fifth year become dominant over them. The males of this subadult group are more peripheral, more assertive and daring in relation to outside events. Apparently, though little evidence exists on this point, the subadult males are split into two categories in their relationship to the adults of the group, some remaining peripheral most of their lives, the others becoming assimilated into a close relationship with the dominant males.

Hamadryas baboon young

Whereas in the savannah baboons up to the age of three years play groups consist of both sexes, in the hamadryas these groups are almost entirely made up of males. (A count of nine such groups, composed of infants and juveniles up to the age of three years, showed a total of forty-nine males and six females.) This difference is obvious already in groups of black infants less than five months old, and comes about because two-thirds of all the hamadryas females from one to three years of age have already become consorts of an adult male. Many become consorts even before the age of one year.

The behaviour pattern which leads to an early consort relation is also one which incorporates the females in the one-male unit. A young adult male will, from time to time, kidnap youngsters who have moved away from their mothers and will nurse them for up to half an hour. This behaviour, like that of some Japanese macaque monkeys and occasionally savannah baboon groups, is initially directed at infants of both sexes. The behaviour itself has both a cradling and a restrictive component in that the kidnapped young-ster is restrained. A little later, the young male turns his attention on to one female, and by repeatedly behaving in this way towards her they get to know one another and adopt one another. His restrictive behaviour then increases and when she strays any distance away he runs after her and picks her up. Her straying more and more agitates him, and eventually he may bite-hold rather than grasp her. This appears to be a breakdown of the usual inhibition on attacking infants, and sometimes leads to the laceration of the head of the infant. During this time her behaviour shows an ambivalence which gradually develops a component of reflected escape towards him in response to a threat from him, or merely a glance at her from him. If these gestures are insufficient, he now retrieves her by rushing at her and giving her a neck-bite. By this time she is incor-porated into his unit and is mating with him. The young female, having been frequently attacked by her consort, will yet run into his arms when threatened by another baboon. She will also ride on her consort's back across passages in the sleeping cliff which, because of her small size, she could not herself negotiate. Thus the young male comes to protect his consort as a mother would her infant. A similar 'maternal' tendency is shown by all hamadryas males to-wards black infants, which they pick up and hug frequently and carry until the leader of the mothers' unit chases them away.

In an interesting experiment carried out by Kummer,[15] five young juveniles of both sexes were trapped at one cliff and released near another group. All were caught and 'mothered' by young adult males of the new group in the described way. Not one of the adult females even tried to take care of any of these juveniles.

Since the one-year-old female is not sexually mature, no copu-lation occurs during the initial phases of the formation of these one-male units. But many female hamadryas show sexual swellings at the age of two, which is a year and a half earlier than in savannah baboon females. Then for the next year, although mating takes place between the males and these young females, no infants are born, as there is no conception for six months. Hans Kummer emphasizes that the hamadryas females are much less mobile socially than females of other species of baboons, so it is worth noting what are the major differences between the upbringing of hamadryas females and females of other species. They are:

1. Hamadryas females do not have any experience of life in juvenile groups and as a result do not readily move out of the one-male groups.
2. These young females are subjected to continual attention-binding aggressiveness by the prospective overlord.
3. They do not have a period as members of a grooming group, their own grooming being restricted to their overlord. In these circumstances it would appear that they do not get practice in grooming behaviour except under tension.

A subadult male at about the age of four still frequently sits in a play group, but rarely participates in the activity. More and more he begins to follow one particular one-male unit. The subadult follower concentrates his attention on the females in the one-male unit, approaching them for grooming and, when not observed by the unit leader, for copulation. His contacts with these females become less frequent and finally cease altogether as he becomes more adult. Instead, he is now frequently in contact with the leader of the unit, whenever the troop is moving; the leader presents to him whenever they change direction. By this time the younger male may have one juvenile female with him, while the older one leads three or four females. The more adult the younger male of the team becomes the more he takes over the direction of the group. As the young male may get arousal reduction from grooming the females and from eventually copulating with some of them, it may be possible that the male leader uses presentation as a means of temporarily reducing the arousal of the younger male towards himself, enabling the younger male to follow him, or the sexual posture may simply be used as a guide stimulus, as the hamadryas male rump is distinctive.

The apes

The gorilla infant and mother

The gorilla infant, whose rate of development is twice as fast as that of the human infant, is nevertheless nearly as helpless during the first two months of its life. Its grasp is so weak that it is unable to hang on to its mother's fur for more than a few seconds at a time. During this early period it does not take notice of any moving object or attempt to reach for things. Correspondingly, the mother cradles her infant in one arm all the time, walking on three limbs. Although by the end of the first month the baby is able to cling long enough to enable the mother to climb trees, she continues to nurse and support her infant for at least another six weeks. At two and a half months it is already quite active, and by four months a lively youngster.

The mother's chest is broad and her belly round, and neither is furry enough for the baby to hold on to. Her broad back, on the other hand, is well supplied with hair, and youngsters find it easy to move about on it, but they are pulled back by the mother and held against her chest whenever she sits or moves off rapidly. This activity diminishes gradually.

Not until it is eight months old does the infant become aware of the slight changes in the mother's behaviour which herald her departure, so that she has to gather it up before moving off. Unlike most other species, the gorilla mother does not groom her infant, and there are no signs of appeasement gestures between mothers. Most striking are two features of the behaviour which probably go together: the first is that both infant and mother appear to like bodily contact with each other for its own sake, as when a youngster comes up to the mother and leans against her or she returns this gesture by placing an arm round her infant's shoulder. There are many other activities which seem to be done for the sake of doing them and it may therefore be assumed that they are enjoyed as well as providing reassurance. The second aspect of the gorilla mother/infant relationship which we must here consider is the possibility that the mother appreciates certain requirements of an infant and alters her behaviour in such a way as to provide them; that is to say, she is not merely responding in one of a number of set ways, but appears to be aware of the nature of the requirement. It is worth looking in detail at the examples of behaviour which suggest this possibility, for if it could be conclusively established, it should be possible, by studying the gorilla mother/infant relationship, to find out how to demonstrate the mother's understanding of the infant.

The first instance concerns feeding behaviour and the way the infant learns from its mother what to sample and eat. In this respect gorilla infants seem to be able to pay much more direct attention to their mothers than, for example, baboons, which merely forage in the same area as their mothers. One gorilla infant was seen to pull down the lip of a female and extract a piece of food and eat it; in this way it obtained a clear idea of what the female was eating. Conversely, a female will actively indicate to the infant what not to eat by removing an unpalatable leaf from its hands. This suggests a recognition of the effect the leaf would have on the infant. In a similar, but more positive, instance a female was seen to watch her infant jerk and pull with both hands at a broken lobelia stem rooted in the ground. After a short while she reached over and snapped the stem off and then laid it on the ground. The infant picked it up and gnawed it.

When an infant slips and the mother reaches out to support it, this could be merely a reflex action, but at times it appears to be more than that. Similarly the attempts by the mother to encourage the young to walk seem to show empathic features. On one occasion a mother placed a three-month-old infant, barely able to crawl, on the ground and then walked slowly ahead of it. In another instance a female, which was being followed by a one-and-a-half-year-old offspring, turned back when the youngster got stuck across a gap between two branches, so that it could neither advance nor retreat. Perhaps more striking still was the case of a female who saw her infant go over and lean against another female and kept it under observation so that, when the other female turned and was about to roll on top of the infant, the mother quickly pulled it away with one arm. Finally, strong evidence that the mother is aware of the needs of her infant is provided by the example of a female which was carrying her eight-month-old offspring with a serious wound on its rump. The infant seemed to be too weak to ride on her back, but it was of an age when she would not normally cradle it in her arms. Nevertheless, she did just this and did it in such a way that no part of the wound touched her body: the infant was continuously held belly downwards, with one of her arms around its waist or with its body draped over her elbow. That she was aware of the wound was apparent from the fact that she once looked at it intently and picked it briefly with one hand. She also kept other animals at bay and did not allow them to touch it.

One of the most engaging aspects of the behaviour of juveniles and infants is the varied nature of their play, which is divided about equally between rough-and-tumble and gymnastic exercises, exploiting the possibilities of hills and branches. Social gambols include wrestling, chasing, follow the leader and 'king of the castle', while gymnastic exercises embrace activities like sliding down hills and swinging from or batting branches. Infants obtain their first social contacts on these occasions.

The chimpanzee mother and young

Jane Goodall[16] was able to get very close to the chimpanzees and to watch the progress of their young from birth. The young chimpanzee is supported by the mother against her belly for most of the first month, like the gorilla. The mother uses her thighs as an alternative way of supporting the young, freeing her hands for other occupations. During brachiation both thighs are drawn up towards the body to provide support on her ventral surface. The infant chimpanzee usually tightens its grip when the mother moves suddenly, but this does not always prevent it from falling. While some mothers are constantly adjusting their position to give support to their youngsters and are quick to clasp them and hold them tight whenever any unusual movement occurs, others are less attentive to their infants. In the later stages of being carried the infant may be seen dangling below the mother's belly, hanging on by its hands (see Plate 15). When seven to eight weeks old, however, the young start to ride the mother's back, mounting from behind as she extends a rear foot, which acts as a mounting pad. The mother frequently restricts her youngster's movement with her hand, pushing it back into her groin when, at about seven to nine weeks old, it first struggles to look around and, later, when it tries to pull itself away from her by means of twigs and grasses. A striking feature of the chimpanzee is the long period for which the young, even the juveniles up to the age of eight years, remain closely associated with their mother. (In some instances this has been reported of the Japanese macaque and the rhesus monkey.)

The close association between the mother and her various off-spring means that the young infant is often the focus of attention of the other members of this mother-family. These attentions may be the first cause of separation of the young from its mother, as when it is removed from her by one of its brothers or sisters. As with the other species of primates, the mother protects her infant from some hazards by keeping it close to her, but a notable feature of the chimpanzee mother's behaviour, and one which stands out in Jane Goodall's report, is the protection that she affords against unfavourable climatic conditions and dangerous situations. She protects her infant not only from falling from her (unlike baboons which only wait if the young become detached), but also from branches, rocks, etc., and from the effects of heavy rain, when she cradles it and hunches over it in much the same manner as she would hunch over it under attack from one of the males of the group. With the young chimp unable to look after itself in the first few months, the hazards of accidents are great and, correspondingly, the mother seems to be much more aware than mother macaques or baboons of those natural forces and situations in which the infant is likely to harm itself. In particular this takes the form of being aware of the effects of gravity and the youngster's inability to support itself, not only on herself, where the reaction could be one of immediate reflex, but in its relationship to the physical environment.

By one and a half years of age the young chimpanzee can usually move easily on the ground and along most branches. Often, however, the mother waits at the lowest branch to carry her infant down a thick trunk or to assist it over some difficult gap. She is quick to reach out if a branch bends under its weight. Even when a branch cracks, she is often quick enough to catch the infant before it falls. This behaviour shows a striking parallel to that instance quoted earlier of the female gorilla snatching her young away from a neighbour who a moment later would have rolled over on top of it. That instance was quoted as one of those likely to show that the mother was aware of the situation of her baby at any one moment, but – looked at in another way – this could be seen as an awareness of the properties of objects in the surroundings and the relationship of her young to them.

There are reasons for believing that awareness of objects as parts of the physical environment is one modality of behaviour in contrast to a modality required to organize social relationships; if so, it is phylogenetically very old. This can be inferred from the work of Segaar and Nieuwenhuys[17] on the breeding behaviour of the three-spined stickleback for those parts of the breeding behaviour, such as care of the nest and eggs, which are oriented towards an aspect of the physical environment and are therefore static, and organized in the mid-brain, whereas those controlling courtship and mating behaviour are organized in the fore-brain. The two categories of behaviour have recently been found in the propensities of rhesus monkeys, some of which perform better in relation to the physical environment and others towards the social environment. These two capacities seem to be combined in the attitude of the chimpanzee towards its young. Not only is it contactually aware of the infant and responding to it in a reflex manner, but this reflex system now includes responses which are capable of supporting the infant, whether in contact with the mother or not. What is new in this situation compared with the behaviour of a baboon mother is the element of anticipation based on a recognition of the infant's relationship to external objects and must, by any criterion, be regarded as an improvement of the mother's awareness towards different aspects of the youngster's behaviour and in a wider variety of situations.

All this takes place in a group in which there is little agonistic behaviour. When agonistic elements do occur they are usually at a fairly low level and do not last long. Hence the conditions in which the young are brought up are altogether much more relaxed than in the societies of baboons and macaques. Together with this goes also a wide variety of new types of behaviour which, because of the low level of agonism, are given a greater opportunity of expression.

The absence of agonistic behaviour is also manifest in that the mother does not behave aggressively towards her young, but rather adopts a denying role, thereby extending behaviour closely similar to physical protection (which has many qualities in common with restraint) into a situation where other species would interfere with the behaviour of the young by being aggressive or threatening it. Even when chimps are aggressive towards older young or juveniles, they frequently follow up the aggression by forms of reassurance, such as embracing them. The mother's resources, however, are not exhausted even by these major differences from the behaviour of monkeys, for she still has it within her power to tickle or groom her children as a means of diverting their attention from some unwanted activity, especially when they are trying to interfere with her playing with, grooming or holding a younger infant. On such occasions she may temporarily leave off the activity that she was pursuing and play with the intruder until it gives what Jane Goodall calls a 'laugh'.

An infant sometimes fails to respond to signals as, for example, when it remains up in a tree after the mother has signalled it to go on. She may then be obliged to climb back towards it, only to receive a smack on her outstretched hand. When the infant is finally retrieved the mother simply pushes it rather roughly but not aggressively into the ventral position, thus forcing the baby to take the right action. Like langur mothers, chimpanzees permit their young to take scraps of food from them, and the young actively beg from their mothers. The chimpanzee, unlike the monkey, mother will continue to divide and share food even with an older offspring. Chimpanzee mothers often spit out the food they are eating on being begged by one of their children, and surrender bananas to them when they touch their mother's hand. But this is not a universal way of behaving towards the interference of the young: other mothers may jerk the food out of reach of the young or even restrain them physically by pinning them down into their lap or often on to their knees. The youngsters, too, differ individually in the extent to which they beg or persistently solicit the mother for food. Some throw tantrums and their mothers are frequently very tolerant of them in these situations, offering food to the screaming infant.

Chimpanzees differ from all the other monkeys and apes we have so far considered, including the gorilla, in that they do not groom the newborn infant except as a continuation of the displacement grooming, which is often self-directed in conflict situations. In the behaviour of baboons grooming is evoked largely in situations of conflict. The same might well be true of the origin of this behaviour when the young chimp is twelve to thirteen weeks old. For at this time the first infant separation from the mother was noticed, when the infant was taken from her by one of its siblings. A situation like this involves the mother in conflict with her other youngsters and this might well be the trigger for commencing grooming, as it was at the same time that the mother began to groom the infant. Once started, however, grooming increases in duration and by ten months the young is presenting itself for grooming and begins to groom the mother. Not until the second year does it develop an adult grooming technique, separating the hairs with one hand, picking at the skin with the other and occasionally using the mouth to remove objects. Grooming bouts become longer, lasting up to fifteen minutes, and grooming gradually replaces play and affectionate behaviour which, up to then, had been (together with grooming) one of the main features of the behaviour between the mother and her young, expressing and probably establishing the bonds which last into later life.

A mother's play, which consists of rolling her infant over, mock-biting and tickling it, gently sparring with it or pushing it to and fro as it dangles from a branch, occurs most frequently when the baby has begun to move about, and Goodall suggests that this first play is at least in part related to a distraction of the infant's attention from the attempts to pursue other forms of behaviour, which the mother would otherwise have to restrain. 'Affectionate' behaviour is probably the most relaxed and the least definite form of behaviour. It is the occasion for the mother to inspect the young in the least disturbing manner; baby chimpanzees are never held at arm's length and groomed, unlike the langur and baboon infants. The chimpanzee mother may put her arm on the back of her infant and, staring into its face, may lift its face up by putting her finger under its chin. All mothers kiss their infants by lightly putting their lips to some part of their bodies from time to time, occasionally kissing the palms of their hands, or they may idly flex and extend the infant's limb while carefully looking at the infant. Most of these affectionate gestures, however, fade out by the time the infant is a year old.

Jane Goodall's account of the behaviour of the young chimpanzees does not mention separation into sex groups which are such a feature of the young of the species Cercopithecidae reported earlier in this chapter. The same is true of George Schaller's description of the social patterns of young gorillas, though infants of both sexes are attracted towards adult males. This tendency becomes less apparent later in life.

CONCLUSION

The young of most subhuman primates cling to their mother at – or shortly after – birth or, like the young of the chimpanzees and gorillas, are cradled by their mother and continue to experience body-contact, which is a continuation of contactual prenatal experience for the young of all eutherian mammals.

Birth for the infant of most primate species is a moment of rapid and, perhaps, physically violent change in its life and is immediately followed by the addition of a new component to its capabilities, the power to cling, by which it retains continuity of bodily contact which provides maximum reassurance. For the young of the chimpanzees and gorillas, however, the experience after birth differs from the rest of the primate stock in one feature. Birth does not coincide with a sharp change in the form of infants' behaviour from a condition of dependency to one of active, self-assertive clinging. The young of both chimpanzees and gorillas, as well as of man, are wholly dependent on the mother for immediate after-birth care, but the ape mothers which provide adequate nursing also provide continuity of bodily contact by cradling of their young, whereas this is not a necessary concomitant of nursing by the human mother. Both bodily contact and the assertive clinging component of behaviour are lacking for the human infant and certainly invest the moment of birth with characteristics wholly different for this species of mammalia; indeed, these characteristics may not have been experienced by the young of our ancestors since the dawn of viviparity in the mammals.

As they grow up, the young of chimpanzees and gorillas experience less rejection (and hence less ambivalence) from their mother than do the young of macaques, though, as far as one can see, this does not prevent the young of macaques and baboons from setting up attachments which are as long-lasting as those in the ape species. By contrast, the status of the macaque, baboon and langur mothers is a more lasting influence on their growing young.

The work of Kaufman on the effects of isolation in the young macaque's behaviour shows that without a mother to turn to the activity and exploratory behaviour of the young suffers; as does in a similar way the behaviour of the infants of low-ranking Japanese macaque and langur mothers, which also brings about a longer period of dependency of the growing infant. This suggests, therefore, that as in these instances the infants are not deprived of their mothers, that it is the quality and perhaps amount of nursing that restores or enhances the subsequent exploratory processes of the infant.

Owing to the presence of other females, and/or in some species interested males, an infant deprived of its mother is not likely to be without adult support in any of the social species studied.

CHAPTER FIVE

The Social Structure of a Population

Sociability of mammals

Much social behaviour is recognizably agonistic. This is to say that it involves aggressive components and flight components simultaneously, or in rapid alternation. At the same time, sexual behaviour, or other forms of social interaction such as grooming, may be brought into the agonistic framework (though an animal can behave sexually, and groom, in a non-agonistic state) as can forms of interaction between two or more animals in which aggression or flight are manifest.

Much behaviour is of course non-agonistic. Our awareness of non-agonistic behaviour has been greatly enhanced by Jane Goodall's studies, which we have just reported, and there is reason to believe that the apes and ourselves share an enlarged capacity for this type of behaviour. But less is known about it, and it is a more recently discovered category than agonistic behaviour. Later in the book, when we deal with the pattern of social relations, we shall be able to indicate some of the relationships between agonistic and non-agonistic behaviour. This chapter outlines what is known about the structure of agonistic sociability in mammals, placing it in a wider context.

Sociability between members of the same species can be recognized by a tendency to cohere. Coherence is not synonymous with proximity between members of a society, but can operate over a limited distance. Two or more individuals may continuously co-ordinate their movements over that distance by visual or vocal means. This is typical of the higher primates, and in other mammals odour plays some part, usually by territory marking, in co-ordinating the behaviour of a territory holder with that of its neighbours.

Coherence is assessed by the length of time the animals are associated in these ways, or the frequency with which they associate in given types of behaviour. Members of different sub-groups achieve this by different means, so that an animal comes to take up a particular role from the position in society occupied by it. The structure of sociability is the structure of inter-related social bonds, based on identifiable processes of signal and response, which bring about the coherence of two or more individuals; for wherever social life is set up and has an obvious functional significance, the animals involved may remain together longer than just for the period during which the activity with a specific function takes place. For example, in a herd of bison a bull will begin to court a cow in oestrus and gradually forms what is known as an 'attending bond' to her, both being on the periphery of the herd. The bull remains with the cow until she reaches the peak of oestrus activity, mates with her, and then moves off to another part of the herd.

So little is known of the structure of most mammal societies that in the following review only the broadest outline of the picture can be drawn. By virtue of the fact that the characteristic feature of mammals is the possession of mammary glands from which the young derive their nourishment from the females, the 'mother-family' is mandatory. Yet, as we have seen, the bond uniting the young to the mother is *not* primarily related to the satisfaction of obtaining nourishment from her, but in the primates is the result of her first providing refuge and a certain form of contactual satisfaction. It is therefore important to emphasize again that the problem of assessing the nature of the bond uniting the members of a cohesive group is different from that of defining the function or functions the group subserves.

R. D. Martin[1] has recently uncovered important anatomical evidence bearing on the origins of the young's ability to cling to the mother. Young that cling to the mother are found in some species distributed in many orders of mammals, including some of the most primitive, and may even have been characteristic of the earliest mammals as a group, especially if these were climbers with grasping extremities, as some embryological evidence suggests.

Another type of social bond is that between a male and female extending over the period of mating. A prolonged pair-bonding lasting over the period of rearing the young does not often occur in the mammals which keep a large number of young in a nest, where they are fully protected.

Diurnal rodents like the rat (*R. norvegicus*) and marmots – both inhabiting burrows in open savannah and woodland country – live in communities of both sexes; on the other hand, the golden hamster appears to be solitary. This is paralleled in the Lagomorphs; e.g. the rabbit is communal and the hare solitary. Arboreal forms are more often solitary, the sexes coming together for mating and the family remaining together only as long as the young are in the nest. This is well illustrated in the family Sciuridae, or squirrels. The grey and red squirrels remain solitary as adults, but the red squirrel male may temporarily defend the nest while it is occupied. The flying squirrel winters as a family band, but this is not a true cohesive unit since the animals are active during the day and in the reproductive season the male plays no part in the defence of the nest.

In the rodents, the shift from forest living to open plain living has involved a change from a diet consisting mostly of roots, seeds and fruits to the utilization of grass, which in turn entails a good deal of time spent in the open. In the ground-squirrel and marmots, both adapted to exploiting open habitats, there is a general increase in social complexity. The area over which rodents range for food may overlap with that of neighbours, but two neighbours avoid each other. All are colonial and defend their individual burrows, but there is no long-term pair-bonding, and the females with their litters form the only organized sub-groups within the colony of marmots. Members recognize each other by smell, but the differentiation within a group is dependent on visual, and probably tactile, clues. Males are related to each other in rank order, established by the possession of a submission posture which reduces the agonistic intensity of an encounter. All members, including females, are familiar members of a group. The society lives within the protection of a burrow, the effectiveness of which is increased by food hoarding.

In free-ranging mammals without a nest as a refuge, the males remain separate from the females. Thus, for example, the all-male bands of the mountain sheep (*Ovis canadensis*) represent another type of bond, for the members of this band act together with the rest of the flock only when defence is involved. Female red deer form cohesive herds which are really collections of mother-families. It is evident that formation of flocks, schools, herds, etc., of both sexes is not necessarily the direct result of cohesion of pairs, or the maternal neonatal relationship, but could be (and often is) a formation by recruitment.

The order Carnivora offers interesting parallel examples with notable differences. This order includes the cats and dogs, which are flesh-eating. Because they are near the top of the food chain, the population density of the carnivora must be much less than that of their prey. Thus they need to be spaced, and spacing behaviour is an important part of their repertoire. One means of effecting dispersal involves the defence of a territory, as we saw in the rodents which occupied savannah country, but another is the formation of a small closed social group with an annual juvenile dispersal, as in the lions; still another is to exhibit a pronounced mutual avoidance or disinclination to form cohesive grouping, e.g. the cheetah. Examples of all these are to be found amongst the carnivora. Working against this tendency, however, is the habit of hunting in packs, as in wolves, jackals, hyenas, etc. The social group here provides the method of obtaining food.

The wide dispersal of a species like the Indian tiger and many other species of cat goes with their peculiar way of holding and utilizing territory in common with neighbours. This is because the territories, although marked by the owners, cannot be readily surveyed. Neighbouring domestic cats who give precedence of passage to a neighbour already moving in a particular shared pathway illustrate that such carnivores are able to tolerate each other's presence at times. This enables neighbouring tigers to share a kill, and some small cats to hunt in sight of each other. Domestic cats frequently come to lie next to each other for an hour or so during the night. Flexibility in the use of territory by different members of the same species is also evident in the way many members do not possess established ranges, but are passing through, ready to take up newly vacated 'lots', or in search of mates.

From this brief review of different orders of the class Mammalia one can see that the population is spread out over the area occupied by it, not evenly but by being broken down into a number of regional local associations of the individuals composing it. These groups

K

within the population may be located at a fixed point or they may move about within a range or territory. If it is a range, the individuals of one group frequently associate fairly readily with members of an adjacent group, but a territory is a defended area and the group is marked as much by a principle of exclusion of neighbouring members from an association with it as by the cohesion it shows between its members. Even where the group is mobile, as in some of the species of subhuman primate we considered in Chapter 3, it may be largely exclusive. But in these instances, too, individuals may pass from one group to another, and while this is done without reference to territory in some subhuman primate societies, in many cats – in the Indian tiger, for example – the inter-relationships between groups may depend upon a territorially very mobile individual or by utilizing territorial shared paths. Hence cohesion and exclusion can be dependent on two basic modalities on which social behaviour is organized: the physical environment and the social dependency of one individual on another.

Four main types of social organization can be recognized.

1. The simplest forms are probably the temporary colonial sleeping groups, the hibernating groups and some temporary feeding aggregates, but these are not groups organizing social behaviour and are probably only the direct result of features of the physical environment. However, there is a high degree of cohesion in the colonies of the ground squirrels, herds of ungulates and the schools of whales and dolphins. It is possible that these are made up of associations of smaller units, the members of which remain together for long periods of time.

2. Liaisons between members of opposite sexes, associated with copulation, may be brief, as in the solitary hamster or the temporary courtship of the herding bison. On the other hand, a more prolonged association between bands of females and bands of males may set the scene for the mating activity of a dominant red deer or wildebeest. Alternatively, the dominant status of the active breeding males may be associated with the temporary breeding grounds set up in the traditional areas by, for example, the Uganda kob.

3. The rarest form of sociability is the long-term association between a male or number of males with many females, forming a heterosexual group, which is found in certain carnivores, ungulates and primates.

4. Of equal importance is the prolonged association between members of one sex, as foreshadowed in the societies of the mammals we have just reviewed, found again as a component of the varied heterosexual groups and societies so characteristic of the primates.

Some functional considerations

When the food is widely and evenly distributed as, for example, with grass eaters, the biological advantage of a cohesive group appears to be related in many instances to the requirements of defence in an open environment. The cohesiveness of the marmot society, which has associations involving both sexes, might be the result of different individuals of the same species living in the same area, exploiting the potentialities in the same way by exploring outwards from a burrow and so feeding always within a safe distance and perhaps being aware of the presence of the other animals and alert to their warning cries. But much needs to be done before we can understand the exact way in which members of these different types of community keep together.

On the other hand, those species which forage over a wide area, moving over their feeding range month by month, require a different set of persistent social bonds to realize the protection afforded by numbers, as they have dispensed with the aggregating effect of a return or escape to the protection of a core area or shelter. In deer, bison and some sheep a bond has developed between the members of one sex. It can therefore be seen that in many instances adaptation for defence or hunting has brought about strong social bonds between members of one sex, and their reproductive associations necessarily take second place. Yet both sexes hunt together in a pride of lions, though it should be noted that there is only one male lion in a social group and he plays a very passive role, the females stalking the prey and driving it towards him. In many defensive associations, however, heterosexual groups are to be found.

Protection against attack plays a prominent part, possibly always a crucial part, in shaping a society: in fact a society might be regarded as a defensive unit of the population in non-predatory species.

Self-limitation of animal populations

It has recently become clear that wild populations living in a restricted area do not, at least for many years at a time, over-exploit their food supply. This must involve a self-limiting mechanism which controls the population density. Wynne-Edwards[2] has put forward the idea that this self-limiting mechanism is built into the social behaviour of the species. Examples of this are now known, although no single instance has been worked out giving clear evidence of his further claim that numbers fluctuate from year to year in step with the available food supply; or, if this is so, how it happens.

Wild populations of rodents are known to fluctuate, the population building up over a number of years and then suddenly undergoing a catastrophic decline. This is true of voles and squirrels. It is also true of the Arctic hare. In a sparse population of these mammals the breeding groups are widely separated and the amount of territorial overlap is small. Hence, the number of encounters between the males of different territories is also small. As the population increases, so the number of encounters between neighbouring territory holders will increase; as a result, agonistic behaviour rises in the population. The males chase intruders back over the territory boundary, and are themselves chased as they intrude into neighbouring territories. As the population grows and foraging areas tend to overlap, this happens more and more frequently. Christian[3] has found that as the density of the wild population rises, so the adrenals increase in size in the population, and at a certain point the activity of the adrenals causes damage to the kidneys and so reduces viability amongst a population of wild mice. In captive conditions this is directly related to the amount of fighting in closed groups. Chitty[4] showed long ago that in circumstances such as these a sudden catastrophic fall in the breeding rate occurs over more than one generation, and that this is due as much to the poor mating performance of the animals whose own infancy has been disturbed as to other factors. It appears, therefore, that the cumulative effect of a number of physiological disturbances accompanying the fights could be responsible for the sudden decline of a population after reaching a certain density, and that subsequent poor mating behaviour keeps it low for a few generations.

The fluctuation in numbers occurs below the level at which an over-exploitation of the food supply would take place, so there is clearly a self-limiting mechanism in operation; the way in which it is related, if at all, to the available food supply has not been demonstrated. Indeed, that it may have little relation to the food available may be inferred from the following evidence.

Lemur populations in Madagascar eat only a small proportion of the available food. Hermit crabs which survived the atom bomb explosion in Eine Wetok atoll in the Pacific have returned to their original density, but are now eating the outer layer of plant stems because their original seaweed food is no longer available in sufficient quantity. Meagre information like this suggests that individuals within a population are capable of reacting to a given population density in such a way as to limit the population at that density, irrespective of food supply.

Collias and Southwick[5] found that the population of howler monkeys in Barro Colorado island rose from 398 to 489 between 1932 and 1933, dropped to 239 in 1951 and rose again to 814 in 1959. The territory of troops which were isolated from one another at low densities expanded, so that boundaries were contiguous during peak densities of the population; this facilitated the spread of infection, which reduced the population.

Studies (Chance, unpublished) of a rhesus colony in which there was a high level of agonistic behaviour showed that the animals of the colony died of mucoid dysentery without accompanying pathogens, while others were infested with shigella dysentery, suggesting that this disease spread in the conditions created by mucoid dysentery. Christian has shown that a population of *Microtus*, starting from a breeding pair, will cease to grow after a certain density is reached. In experiments carried out by his team, while the numbers *born* remain about the same, the numbers *weaned* diminished rapidly to the point where the population became stable. Bruce[6] has shown that the smell of strange males induced anovulation and/or resorption of embryos in pregnant mice; thus a mechanism capable of controlling density of population by reduced fertility and/or viability undoubtedly exists, at least in some species. It is now known that the reduced viability affects low-ranking animals.

Differential well-being

Individuals or groups of some species range over a much wider area than that to which they can claim exclusive possession and which may be defended by them; for other species or at other times, if the density of the population varies the range coincides much more closely to the defended territory. In a wild population territories vary in size, and hence a differential access to available food supplies arises. Rank order also establishes differential utilization of food resources between members of a group. The best example is provided by the work of Murton[7] and his colleagues. They studied the nature of the social interaction in flocks of feeding pigeons and were able to show that this affected their rate of feeding, so that animals shot at dusk when they were about to roost for the night were found to have their crops filled to varying extents. Those low in rank were less well fed.

Now let us look at the mechanism of social interaction and its effect on feeding. The sight of a feeding pigeon attracts others, and in this way flocks of pigeons assemble, for example, on clover leys. They move over the ground at a constant rate, pecking at the individual leaves of clover. One peck, therefore, represents the ingestion of one clover leaf. By observing the rate of pecking through binoculars, it is possible to establish the rate of the intake of food. Now, pigeons joining the flock may land in the centre or at the edge of the flock; the fast feeders, it was observed, were found in the centre and slow ones at the edge; the slowest near the front edge. This happens because those landing near the front of the group constantly look back towards the advancing group, and this activity interrupts their feeding, whereas those in the centre seem relatively unperturbed by the presence of their neighbours. This is a clear example of how the deflection of attention towards more dominant animals interferes with the feeding activity of subordinate birds, and it turns out that usually the subordinate animals only manage to take in enough food to carry them over the night. They are destined to succumb if conditions deteriorate, as, for example, when the night temperature drops steeply. It is equally important, however, that the differential distribution of food keeps a few birds in a really well-fed state and capable of breeding as soon as conditions improve. After a catastrophic fall in the numbers of animals with individual territories, the survivors are much less capable of re-establishing contact between one another, and are thus not likely to restore their numbers rapidly in more favourable conditions.

Maintenance of a continual differential access to food, shelter,

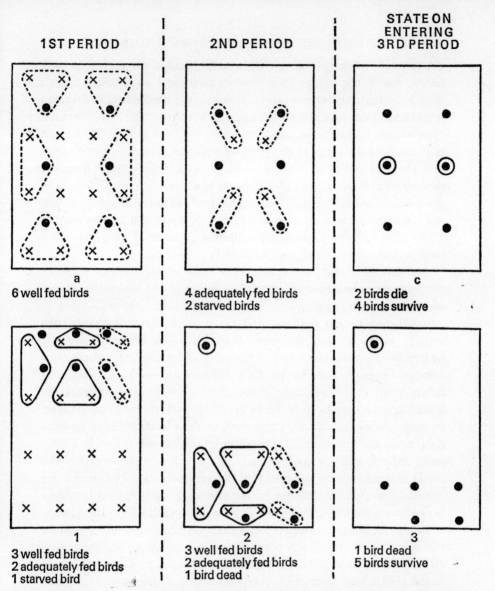

1ST PERIOD	2ND PERIOD	STATE ON ENTERING 3RD PERIOD
a	b	c
6 well fed birds	4 adequately fed birds 2 starved birds	2 birds die 4 birds survive
1	2	3
3 well fed birds 2 adequately fed birds 1 starved bird	3 well fed birds 2 adequately fed birds 1 bird dead	1 bird dead 5 birds survive

Equal access top row, no flock formation. Unequal access bottom row, rank-ordered flocks.

X X = units of food   ● ● = live birds   ⊙ ⊙ = dead birds

Well fed birds eat two units of food per period : adequately fed, one unit.

Death of one bird by starvation early on leads to longer maintenance of the rest of the flock.

FIGURE 7: Showing the mode of operation by which rank-ordered groups of pigeons consume food unevenly, with consequent prolongation of breeding potential. (*After Murton, Isaacson and Westwood*)

females, etc., brought about by the differentiation within a rank order, would appear to have certain biological advantages, which may have been one of the factors selecting for sociability. A diagram is included here to show how it comes about that such a differential distribution of food is advantageous as a survival mechanism for the flock as a whole to meet changing conditions. The mode of feeding and the differential well-being within a rank order appear as safety devices to prevent over-exploitation of the food resources. This does not mean that exceptional seasonal fluctuation in the food supply will not sometimes lead to starvation, but, if so, there will always remain a few very well-fed animals immediately capable of breeding when food supplies increase again (see Figure 7, p. 151).

Animals of a high status are in a state of well-being; those of medium status are merely adequately fed; and the very subordinate animals are undernourished. This differential state of well-being in a population means that in hard times, with few individuals continually optimally fed, the state of well-being is being maintained nearer the more affluent end of the rank order and stays there over a large range of conditions. This differential, however, may also reflect a differential response to the social stimulus of aggregation. It is well known that in some birds breeding performance is enhanced by aggregating on nest sites and that, under the stimulus of association, they are brought into breeding condition more nearly at the same time. Equally, it is clear that those which respond negatively to social conditions and are thus low in rank order are excluded from breeding, so that this differential response existing between the members of a group produces a rank order relationship within the group.

The evidence therefore suggests that self-limiting devices exist in the agonistic relations of a population, and that these devices reside either in the defensive/offensive balance between territory holders or in the threat and submission relations within a defensive unit (rank order) which has thereby encapsulated the self-limiting mechanism within itself. In primate societies, as we shall see, these two different situations co-exist and may interact.

Variation within a population

The differentiation in behaviour which places different individuals in an order of rank, and consequently places them in a different

152

relationship to the environment, is only one aspect of that variation within a population which is a fundamental attribute of all living things. This variation can be continuous, as in the differences in sensitivity to the same stimulus. It is true of most animals that mild stimuli bring about positive approach responses, whereas intense stimuli cause withdrawal. Hence, differential sensitivity may lead the same stimulus to cause an approach response in one individual and a withdrawal response in another, and intermediate ambivalent tendencies may exist. In this way a population tends to consist of two or more types of individuals. Such a split in the population can become established by learning, and this could be the mechanism responsible for the differentiation between sub-groupings within age and sex categories of Japanese macaques, though Itani[8] has identified a number of individual traits that contribute to the success in establishing high rank.

No full assessment of the contributory factors placing an individual at a certain point in the rank order relations has yet been made. Apart from the predisposition of the individual, learning has been demonstrated to play some part, and can be expected either to keep an individual at a particular place in the rank order or to facilitate and determine the position which he ultimately achieves during his maturation. A split may, however, become hereditarily fixed in a proportion of the population, as in the populations of the deer-mouse (*Peromyscus*). Some species of this rodent develop a rigid escape seizure pattern in adolescence in about 5 per cent of the population, which appears to have survival value in extreme situations. Unpredictable, because erratic, escape replaces normal escape behaviour (which would lead the animal back to its burrow), and has survival value for a population rather than the individual. A population of this kind is di-ethic with respect to its escape behaviour; that is to say, the species possesses alternative forms of behaviour for the same type of situation.

There are many instances where it is possible to see that the presence of the other sex provides a positive stimulus not only towards mating, but towards the enhancement of the readiness to mate; e.g. the clumping of birds in the nesting season brings each bird into reproductive activity at the same time, and the female macaques undergo a prolongation of oestrus when consorting with a dominant male. This propensity to mate is itself dependent on the internal secretion of the appropriate hormones which, through their protein anabolic effect, bring about a greater bodily efficiency, including resistance to disease, and, in the female, a deposition of food reserve in the form of fat, especially during pregnancy. The specific advantages which arise from the sexes remaining together for a long period of time are, for example, the warning cries and protection that the males can give to the females, the effects of differentiated roles (especially in promoting the greater care that the mother can give to the young) and the ease with which mates are found and numbers replenished, as in rodent groups. But, in addition, there will be the physiological advantages that accrue to all bodily functions from a persistent, if subliminal, mating arousal. Whenever, therefore, specific behavioural advantages – such as the protection afforded to the female by persistent association with the dominant male – lead to the persistent association between the sexes, there is added to it the selective advantages just mentioned. These will maintain the association even when the initial behavioural advantages may be reduced, provided there is no contrary selection.

In view of the tendency for societies involving the persistent association of the sexes to develop in a number of the different mammalian orders – for example in the lions, rodents and primates – it is a reasonable supposition that this interaction between specific behavioural requirements and physiological benefits may have contributed to the development of the societies of both sexes in these orders. In a different way it would also operate towards establishing an extended period of sexual activity, so typical of the catarrhine primates, provided there are not compensatory selective disadvantages.

Escape

Escape usually takes an individual back to a refuge within its territory, not just away from the threat. The young primate escapes to its mother, who acts as the refuge, and its own behaviour in clinging on to her, as well as the care and mothering it may get, not only give it physical protection, but much more often reassure it and enable it to go out into society again. In a society of monkeys there is, as we have seen, always somebody to run to, even if not the actual mother, but in the world of territorial mammals escape is normally along well-trodden pathways to home; e.g. the rat.

Protean behaviour

Mammals as a whole have inherited a form of erratic behaviour designed to take the place of escape to a known refuge, not so much by shaking off the pursuit of a predator as by forcing the predator to lose track of the prey by fractionally delaying its response because of the prey's startling and unpredictable behaviour; this makes the chances of capture less likely. As it turns out, this erratic behaviour has many forms and is not uniformly present in all members of the population, which enhances the unpredictable element in encounters between members of a species and their predators. This behaviour also possesses an instantaneous spontaneity which achieves its effect by disrupting the prey's usual escape behaviour, thereby disturbing the continuity which, in all other types of behaviour, is essential to success.

A variety of insects such as butterflies show erratic behaviour all the time they are moving around, since the predator may appear at any instant from behind cover. But in mammals that have either a territory or a social environment in which they are at all times oriented within points of reference, this type of behaviour would only interfere with other forms of activity, and it is therefore only in unfamiliar situations, e.g. attack or when there is destruction of the environment or (in a situation somewhat similar) when under attack outside their range, that it is manifested. This behaviour has been called 'protean' by Chance and Russell.[9]

Protean behaviour is that aspect of escape behaviour which is sufficiently unsystematic to prevent a predator predicting in detail the position and/or the actions of the actor. Such behaviour often appears to be quite random, but it is not random in the sense that the protean acts of the actor are functionally connected with the behaviour of the reactor. They are connected in a biologically systematic manner – a manner which is at the same time so structured as to appear unsystematic to the reactor.

Humphries and Driver[10] gave this definition, and Chance and Russell suggest that protean behaviour works by disturbance either of the predator's orientation mechanism or its mood. Escape behaviour has five main protean components, any one or more of which may be combined in the escape behaviour system. Fleeing, for example, can include a number of unsystematic zig-zags, and in mammals this is frequently combined with bouncing and leaping in peculiar ways. Sudden extension of a limb or sudden clonic movements involving alternating extension or flexion of the limbs give rise, in more co-ordinated forms, to sudden leaps backwards or sideways or forwards. (Unexpected attacks in some species may arise from forward pounces being combined with seizing with the jaws or grasping with the hands.) Bouncing has a directionally unpredictable component which is distracting, and because sudden unsystematic events are frightening for many animals it may also have a deterrent effect. The initial immobility and subsequent distracting and unpredictable movements can be seen in an escaping hare, but in contrast, when a number of animals are under attack the scatter of the group may provide an element of distraction. This may also occur in a special form in which the behaviour of first one individual and then another of the group acts as a lure to draw the pursuit away from the others.

The protean behaviour of *Peromyscus* reveals a mechanism to be present which is manifest in only a proportion of the individuals and which has been found to depend on a specific biochemical defect acting as a trigger in these individuals. The mechanism is therefore likely to be present in every individual but is only manifest in those possessing the biochemical trigger. Its value is for the survival of the population, but at the expense of the integrity of responsiveness in the individual, because it introduces an erratic component into the repertoire of the individual.

When it appears in escape behaviour, the erratic component is a supplementary feature by virtue of its capricious nature. But, as we shall see, escape becomes turned back towards the centre of the society in many subhuman primate species and this directional reflection of escape becomes a socializing influence. Then the introduction of erratic components would have a disrupting effect on the continuity of social relations.

CHAPTER SIX

The Interpretation of Subhuman Primate Social Life

The stem structure of subhuman primate society

Both Eisenberg[1] and Carpenter[2] have pointed out that societies are not mere random aggregations, but that the structure of the society is in large part due to the tendency of the members to remain together or to cohere. On this criterion subgroups within a society can be recognized. Three main sub-groups are widely distributed amongst subhuman primate societies: assemblies of females and young, clusters of juveniles and cohorts of adult males.

Common to many different species is the sub-group consisting of the female and her young; and several of such units, together with attached females without young of their own, constitute the *female assemblies*. Such assemblies are a very prominent feature of langur society, where, as we have seen, the infant is passed from one female to another from very early life while the troop is stationary, but each infant is collected by its mother when on the move. Female assemblies are, therefore, more evident at those periods of the day when the troop is not engaged in major activities such as feeding, moving from one locality to another, or on the run from danger. The rhesus mother, on the other hand, remains detached from other females for several weeks at least after the birth of her infant and only permits it to move away from her after about six weeks, at which time she enters the assemblies of females which act as a centre of attraction for other, childless, females, some acting as 'aunts' to the young. As we have seen, adolescent or subadult females and females without young participate in these assemblies, grooming each other, playing with the young and sitting together, often watching particular young for opportunities to collect and nurse them.

Female assemblies are found as a prominent feature in the rhesus, the Japanese macaque, the langur, the savannah and gelada baboons, the patas monkey, the chimpanzee and gorilla. The exceptions are the bonnet macaques, in whose society the grooming relations are so widespread and random that they tend to obscure any preferential assemblies there may be. The association between the females of a hamadryas one-male group might be regarded as an expression of the same tendency, were it not that the attention of the females is confined to members of the one-male group. Since gibbon pairs remain isolated from others, it is not possible for female assemblies to form in gibbon societies. The exceptions, therefore, are in species in which a special social structure precludes the formation of female assemblies. We may therefore conclude that the widespread occurrence of female assemblies represents a modality in the sub-grouping tendencies of subhuman primate society.

The term assembly has been used to describe the female sub-groups in order to emphasize that their structure is less rigid than that of the cohorts of males; and clearly the structure varies greatly from species to species. In the instances in which the relationship of the females to the males is fluctuating as in rhesus society (in which the females form temporary consort relations) any inherent characteristics of the relationships between females will be less evident. In langur society, on the other hand, where the female assembly is largely separate from adult male interference, it is easier to see the relationship between females *per se*, and it is clearly rank-ordered with enhanced escape motivation typical of the lower-ranking members. Simonds[3] has pointed out that the female assemblies, like the cohorts of males are capable of forming ranked structures of much the same kind, and that the mother lineages that have been reported for Japanese macaque society and by Walter Angst[4] for the colony of *Macaca fascicularis* at the Basel Zoo are an additional element structuring the society.

As the young become largely independent of their mothers, they join together with others of their own age and with juveniles of all ages to constitute another major sub-group: the *juvenile clusters*. Clusters of juveniles in play may be seen together at all hours of the day, foraging as well as playing, as langur juveniles do, and even rushing into each other's arms and carrying one another on their backs, as do juvenile baboons and rhesus monkeys in captive colonies when they are under threat from dominant members of the group.

The members of this juvenile sub-group have a social mobility in some species which they do not possess in others. The juveniles of the hamadryas as well as the gelada baboons move freely between the groups, and may make contacts with juveniles of other one-male groups. Except when they are kept to the periphery of the group as a whole, as in the Japanese macaque groups, and in the societies of chimpanzee, gorilla, rhesus and bonnet macaques, the juveniles are often tolerated near adult males and, until their antics become too boisterous or too close to the females, they are not interfered with.

The juveniles of the patas monkey are always found close to (and, indeed, would seem to be part of) the female assembly, separated from the male of the group; except in play, therefore, they are not easily distinguishable as a separate sub-group. In gorilla groups they move freely between adults of both sexes and at times are clearly visible as a cluster during play together.

The juvenile sub-group is absent from the gibbon society, though it is tempting to think that individuals which intrude into the territory of a neighbouring pair and are chased back by other juveniles, even through their own territory in retaliation, do so partly from a tendency to set up relationships with individuals of their own age.

The third component is the *cohort of males*. Adult males of a cohort remain persistently in each other's company and show some rank order characteristics.

The cohort is synonymous with the males of the breeding hierarchy in the macaques (rhesus, bonnet and Japanese), the gorilla groups and in the heterosexual groups of the savannah baboons. In the heterosexual groups of these species there are no more than seven males in the cohort. Less is known of the form of association between males in the bachelor bands, since although the males of the male bands of gelada remain together and distinct even when they merge with the males of the heterosexual group, little is known of their behaviour when separate from this group. It is not known whether they are rank-ordered. Rank order appears to be present in the bachelor bands of the langurs studied by Sugiyama, but we know nothing of the structure of the patas bachelor bands whose existence has been no more than confirmed by Hall.

Less is known about these all-male bands than about the other two components of the subhuman primate societies, and more attention should be paid to this aspect of the different societies in future work. Male bands are a complementary feature of those societies in which the female assemblies associate either with a cohort of breeding males or where these assemblies are grouped round a single breeding male. The gibbon, because of the equal sex ratio in the heterosexual groups and its 'monogamous' habit, is the only species we have considered which does not possess any of the main features we have been describing.

More evidence is required to identify the processes leading to the break-up of the cohort and to the re-assortment into bisexual family groups, as in chimpanzee societies. Cohorts of this kind can be identified in many species of subhuman primates. When they are present, they are integrated with the rest of the society in specifically different ways. The patas and langur male cohorts are persistently separated from the one-male heterosexual groups. Crook[5] found that while remaining separate much of the time, the male bands of the gelada baboon would retain their spatial identity during the periods when they joined with the collections of one-male groups constituting the rest of the society. Reynolds and Reynolds[6] report that chimpanzee cohorts often spend several days away from the rest of the society. At the other extreme, the gorilla male cohort is integrally part of the heterosexual band. An intermediate category is found in a number of different species such as the Japanese macaque, the Indian macaque and the savannah baboon, in which the male cohorts are, in various ways, spatially distinct within the heterosexual group.

Although there are exceptions, aspects of which will be discussed later, these three main sub-groups constitute together and in their interactions what may be called the 'stem structure' of subhuman primate society, encompassing the social relations of the adults of both sexes, with the juvenile clusters forming a transitional stage in the growth from infancy to adulthood. This concept is schematically presented in Figure 8, and is equivalent to a generalized sociogram for subhuman primate societies. The sub-groupings represent pre-

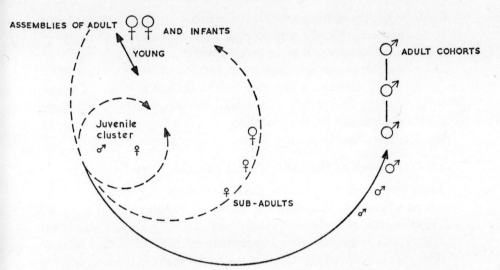

FIGURE 8: The social structure and development of relationships in a generalized group of subhuman primates

ferential associations, or what is in effect a type of social bond, the nature of which must be understood before it is possible to see how various social functions are the outcome of the groupings within a society. These bonds are themselves the result of signals given out by individuals and the capacity of other individuals to respond, both of which are revealed by a knowledge of the individual's social repertoire.

Idiosyncrasies and lability of groups

All societies of higher mammals are composed of individuals whose hereditary predispositions vary greatly. The individual members of one small group or society may therefore possess an adult repertoire consisting of a different set of elements from another group, and circumstances of development and accidental death may result in a group being led by an unusual individual, deficiencies in whose behaviour may cause, by imitation, corresponding deficiencies in the social behaviour of the group. Moreover, some young and subordinate individuals may learn specific habits, and these may be partially transmitted through the group by imitation. All these features have been reported for a population of Japanese macaques.

Moreover, Kummer's study of the hamadryas baboon[7] shows that, for example, the one-male unit is either in a state of growth, maturity or decline, and this will tend to alter from time to time the ratio of individuals occupying a given role. Rowell[8] has also suggested that societies of savannah baboons are structured differently when they live in woodlands and when they live in the open. If this is so, we need to know how much a savannah baboon society differs from a chimpanzee society, the members of which behave differently in woodland and in the open.

The structure of the individual's social repertoire

As we have seen, a complex network of distinct possibilities of action has now been established in the more advanced species of primate. These innate propensities provide each individual with a certain variety and scope of action but it is structured action. Let us consider this concept of structure in the individual's behaviour first by analogy with comparative anatomy.

It is recognized that we possess a skeleton based on the same plan as that of all other vertebrates, so that when some new feature, such as a false palate separating the nasal air passages from the mouth, is developed in mammals we are able to identify the bones in the palate of a reptile out of which this new feature has been constructed. The structural affinities of any particular bone we like to choose can thus be worked out between man and any other vertebrate.

This has a direct bearing on understanding the way posture is achieved. Until we understand that the flexibility of the backbone common to all vertebrates was established for the swimming movements of a fish, and was later rigidified by muscular action, as in the backbone of the horse, rather than by fusion of the bones, as in the bird, we shall not appreciate how much more complex are the postural mechanisms of a mammal compared with those of a frog or bird. Comparative studies are therefore an essential part of any attempt to build up a picture of the structure underlying the social behaviour of all mammals, including ourselves. The different forms of social organization in the primates can only be understood against the background of the evolution of social behaviour in other mammals, from which it will be possible to assess the stem structure of the individual's social repertoire. Specialization can then be seen as a modification of this stem structure.

Let us consider what we mean by behaviour typical of a species. Think for a moment of what we all know of the difference between the way a dog and a cat behave towards a prey which has gone to earth in a hole in the ground. The dog destroys the prey's refuge, digging vigorously with its forepaws and shovelling the loosened earth away with its hindfeet, periodically breaking off to scrape the accumulated heap farther away with its forepaws. The cat, on the other hand, sits watching, ready to spring and catch its prey when it re-emerges. A cat also uses its forepaws to shift soil, but mainly to dig a small hole preparatory to defaecation and afterwards to cover the spot with loose soil. Characteristics of behaviour like these, which we all recognize, represent innate tendencies to respond in different ways to the same stimulus; and there may be differences, too, in performing the same type of behaviour. In the adult, these represent fixed propensities to behave in certain ways which may or may not be dependent either on 'learning', by imitation, or on practice to assist their full development. We shall also have to discuss how far and in what way they are modifiable in the adult.

A number of well-known workers in physiology, biology and ethology have shown that there are intrinsic nervous activities which have a structural organization of their own. Paul Weiss[9] distinguishes the following levels at which such organized complexes can be found.

1. The level of the individual motor unit.
2. All the motor units belonging to one muscle.
3. Co-ordinated functions of muscular complexes relating to a single joint.
4. Co-ordinated movements of the limb as a whole.
5. Co-ordinated movements of a number of locomotor organs, resulting in locomotion.
6. Postures and acts of the animal as a whole.

Acts and postures are gestalt patterns recognized by ethologists.

Behaviour consists of one activity following another. Many people think that 'what happens next' in behaviour must depend on what goes on around them, in the belief that behaviour is entirely dependent on the changing stimuli of the environment. However, once a suitable situation has been chosen in which some pattern of behaviour is repeated, the elements, acts and postures of an animal can be observed, identified and labelled. After this process (which may take a considerable time) is complete, the sequence of each episode can be recorded for subsequent analysis.

Social behaviour which involves the interaction of two animals requires two observers only if the correlation between the behaviour of one animal and another is under investigation, so that the stimulus or signal value of the components is being investigated. Here we are concerned only with the structure of an individual's repertoire as seen in the repeated sequences which reveal the pathways of responses available to the animal, or in what sequences the animal uses any given set of acts and postures.

This type of analysis has not yet been applied in any of the studies of subhuman primate behaviour, and so we shall have to build up our ideas of the structure of social repertoires from studies made on other mammals, notably the laboratory mouse and rat studied by Chance and Mackintosh[10] and Grant.[11] We shall then build up a picture of the likely behaviour structures to be found in some primates from indications derived from other less rigorous studies. This has the advantage that some idea of how the structure of the individual's social repertoire has evolved can be gained by comparison of the behaviour of a number of different orders of mammals. The method will be illustrated by the analysis of interactions between two male laboratory rats (a diadic interaction) after their activity cycle has been reversed so that they are awake during the period of observation (for the convenience of the observer), by keeping them in an enclosure in dim light during the day and bright light at night for a fortnight beforehand.

A pathway of response is made up of the most frequent set of acts which lead to a consummatory act. For example, 'sniff' at the anogenital region, 'follow' the retreating rat (the sequence is the same between males as between males and females) and 'mount' constitute the recognizable components of the male mating behaviour. The agonistic components of an encounter in a cage, however, are less easily distinguishable.

In the many species of mammals capable of setting up a rank order which is based on the continual presence of the members of the rank order close to one another, the individuals possess a mechanism, a series of mutually understood signals, that terminate an aggressive interlude without withdrawal when one animal submits to another – the consummatory act of social flight.

The submission posture of the rat is to lie on its back. The companion straddles it in the full aggressive posture. The signal value of the submission posture is revealed by the fact that the animals separate and pursue non-social activities before re-engaging in an encounter. The acts leading to a submission posture are ambivalent as a result of a balance between aggressive and submissive tendencies in the social flight pathway.

On other occasions one rat will crouch with another grooming its neck, and the postures leading up to this consist of turning first its head and then its body away from the other animal before crouching. This crouching will disappear if the encounter takes place in a large room, where it is replaced by true escape to a refuge (Figure 9).

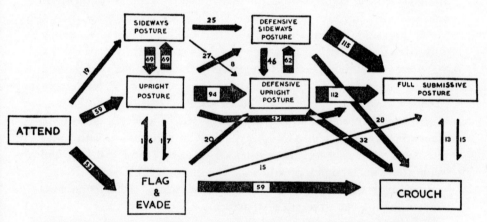

FIGURE 9: Diagram of the flight pathways recorded during encounters between two rats. The diagram demonstrates an escape pathway leading from Attend through Flag and Evade, to *Crouch* (blocked escape), and a social submission pathway leading from Attend through alternating Sideways and Upright postures to Full Submission. The numbers indicate the relative frequency with which each pathway is used. (*See Grant, 1963*)

Chase by the aggressor and escape by the flight-motivated rat occur as consummatory activities on the escape pathway. These are rarely seen in a cage because there is so little space that the full flight response takes place infrequently, and instead the animal retreats under the only shelter provided – the food hopper; but even this is often replaced by crouch. Neither retreat nor crouch in these circumstances lead to a separation of the rats.

Hence it becomes clear that there is a bifurcated flight pathway, consisting, first, of one route leading to social submission, when two animals remain next to each other (top pathway), and second, an escape pathway which separates the animals completely (bottom pathway). These two are distinct pathways of response.

The aggressive rat's behaviour is less stereotyped than that of the submissive rat. This means that the flight-motivated member of the pair is determining the course of the interaction between them, and that at the same time as it reaches a consummatory submissive situation itself it provides a consummating signal to its social partner. Aggression does not – except at high intensities – disperse animals of the same species, but rather brings them together. In a variety of ways it is held in balance with flight tendencies, and this balance is manifest during combat by ambivalent postures such as the upright and sideways postures of the rat.

Mating also brings animals together, and so does a tendency towards social investigation which has not yet been fully analysed by the present method. These three aspects of the behaviour (aggression, mating and investigation) modulate the approach tendencies (though they may themselves be in conflict with each other for control of the final common pathway) but, above all, sociability depends on a sufficient availability of social submission. Otherwise the flight tendency will be expressed in escape and the rats will separate. This complex of submission, combined with social investigation, aggression and mating, is the structure of social behaviour known for the rat – the SIAM structure.

By allowing the rats to meet in an open environment the posture 'crouch' disappears because it is due to blocked 'escape'. Therefore the conflict on the escape pathway when the rat crouches in a cage is due to the fact that escape is not possible, whereas the conflict on the social pathway leading to full submission arises because of two contradictory tendencies (approach/withdrawal) within the rat itself. At any one moment one rat will be giving a defensive form of the sideways or upright postures (which occur on the pathway to full submission) in response to an offensive form by the other rat. The balance may then swing in the opposite direction and the one on the

166

defensive may become offensive, and vice versa. Exact forms of these offensive and defensive postures have been identified. As a result we can say that the final posture is the outcome of the conflict between the tendency to become aggressive and the tendency to flee, and the different forms of sideways and upright posture are an expression of these ambivalent tendencies. The coexistent opposing tendencies are responsible for this ambivalence as well as for the assumption of the submissive posture.

The existence of these opposing tendencies in an animal's behaviour is confirmed by the presence of spatial oscillation in the pathway leading to submission, but this is absent in the escape behaviour which leads to crouch. Both 'flag' and 'evade' (as parts of escape) are stepwise partial and irreversible stages in the movement towards the completely blocked form of escape. The rat turns its head and its body away from the other animal and then crouches.

Comparative morphology of agonistic social repertoire

Examples can be found of different levels of complexity in the individual's social repertoire, and those that have been studied include mice, rats and species of subhuman primates.

The analysis of close combat between two rats has shown that a submission posture terminates the social flight pathway. This means that from the start the subordinate rat is able to terminate the encounter from time to time and the repetition of encounters terminated by submission rapidly reduces the intensity of these interactions, so that the two rats are very quickly able to set up a stable relationship between themselves. A rat quickly learns to behave submissively to a companion but is, in effect, always testing the stability of its own status relationship to that of others in the colony.

In contrast to rats, mice do not have a social submission posture, that is to say, a posture which specifically terminates agonistic social encounters. Instead, one mouse flees from another, stops and adopts a defensive upright posture, temporarily inhibiting the pursuit of the aggressor, which starts to adopt an attacking posture, the offensive sideways. As soon as the pursuer closes in on the defensive mouse, the defender flees again and is chased by the pursuer. This ding-dong goes on until some adventitious circumstance (e.g. distraction of one mouse or the interference of cover) temporarily stops it. In the wild, this type of behaviour is used to chase other mice back to their own territory. Then the balance is struck by one mouse pushing the boundary farther away from its home base and nearer to that of its neighbour. This boundary is stabilized, and the boundaries of the territory fixed, by reference to the physical surroundings.

If the rat differs from the mouse in having a built-in submission posture at the end of a pathway of response whereby it keeps a balance in its relation with a more dominant rat, there is, in addition to this, a new twist to the escape pathway seen in the behaviour of baboons and macaques which turns them back towards a more dominant monkey and also makes them move towards it. They, in fact, escape *towards* the more dominant animal. Both Seward[12] and Grant have noted a tendency for rats to stay near the dominant animal, so reflected escape may be merely a development of this. Kummer has found this reflected escape, especially in the female hamadryas baboons, and it is equally characteristic of the males in the rank order of breeding male macaques. Kummer says:[13]

> During expression of fear, the frightened individual does not remain where it was threatened. Either it flees from the cause of its fear, or it seeks out an animal of the highest possible rank. When fear is intense, the latter invariably happens... It seeks out the highest ranking of the animals present, though this individual himself has been the cause of its fear.

The pattern of agonistic behaviour just described is typical of the macaques and baboons living in open country and is part of the defensive behaviour for meeting danger in this open habitat. It is also combined with a high level of aggressive behaviour organized, as we shall see in the next section, down the hierarchy. Threats from dominant animals may therefore keep agonistic arousal high and, in so doing, help to keep the members closely clustered round the dominant male. To the extent that this state of affairs persists, a constant conflict arises between the tendencies to be social in different ways which an approach to the dominant males engenders and it also disrupts other activities. The behaviour of a subordinate animal which comes close to a more dominant one under these orienting influences shows evidence of conflict and ambivalent behaviour. The subordinate animal is torn between the tendencies of the SIAM system:

aggression, mating, investigation and that part of escape which is reflected back towards the more dominant monkey. Negative and positive tendencies are still present, but are held together in this orientation.

We have here a requirement of safety which has developed a compulsive quality evident especially in the behaviour of macaques and baboons. This becomes still clearer when it is realized that even when a threat is directed at a subordinate by a more dominant animal, the subordinate animal is under a compulsion to move towards the source of this threat.

Little wonder that in this situation of conflict for the individual many stereotyped forms of behaviour appear, which have, in part at least, the function of temporarily preventing the animal from precipitating an open attack upon itself. These forms of behaviour involve compulsive and fixed motor patterns: in captive colonies displaced grooming movements give rise to scratching of the ground surface; yawning (which in the baboons has become a ritual display of the canines); and various ways of cutting off direct visual awareness, such as looking away and glancing back, or looking fixedly at small objects.

The trend shown by the comparative morphology of agonistic social behaviour is now apparent (see Figure 10, p. 170). As the need for more persistent sociability increases it is achieved not by increasing the strength of the approach drives, but in the first stage by blocking escape by means of submission, built into an agonistic social repertoire, typified in the rat's behaviour. In the macaques and baboons this is supplemented by turning back their escape tendency towards the aggressor, so converting withdrawal into approach. This latter change, however, could not have been achieved without the provision of a submission posture for agonistic situations; the baboon and macaques possess a number, two of which are crawling up and lying in front of another animal, and sexual presentation.

By analysing the repertoire of one animal we discover that there are sequences of acts and postures constituting pathways of response, and that these manifest the underlying social tendencies. Such social tendencies impose a fixed manner on an animal and may be more or less active at any one time. They are always organized towards a social partner, and we can see that the difference between the social

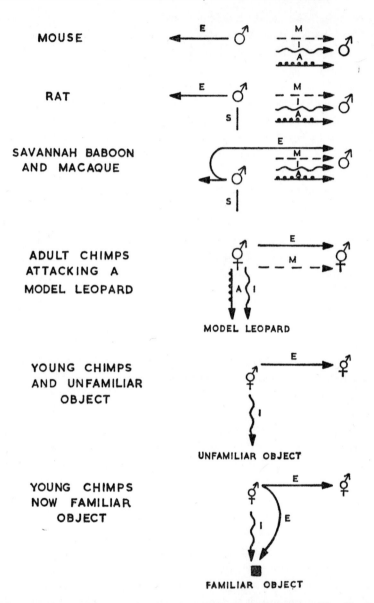

FIGURE 10: Comparative morphology of agonistic social behaviour. The diagram shows the predominant orientation of different social tendencies, which include investigation, and illustrates how escape is an orienting component opposite to positive social tendencies in the mouse and rat, but not in the macaque, baboon and chimpanzee (e=escape, m=mating, i=investigation, a=aggression, and s=submission)

behaviour of a mouse, rat and monkey lies in that they are impelled to make contact with companions by a different set of social propensities. The rat and the monkey can, by virtue of possessing social submission postures, maintain social relations under agonistic conditions which for mice disrupt social relations. Male mice can put up a defence under attack, but separate when agonistic encounters become too severe; subordinate male rats can terminate the encounter by reducing its severity, while not losing touch with the other individual. Subordinate savannah baboons and macaques become fixated on a more dominant male, because every tendency impelling them to move is oriented with reference to him.

So far, the evidence has enabled us to draw up a picture of the way in which social behaviour orients an individual towards a companion when different social propensities are brought into play in agonistic situations. This is expressed mainly in the relations between adult males, whose behaviour is typically rank-ordered. We must now look more closely into this type of bond so as to construct the way in which social bonds, linking members of sub-groups, can be developed out of the behavioural propensities of the individual.

The structure of attention

The social attention of the individuals within a cohort separated from the rest of the society must be directed exclusively at the other members of it. The possibility arises, therefore, that even when they are an integral part of the complete society, distinct coherence of a cohort of males may depend on their maintaining a predominant degree of attention towards themselves. A situation precisely like this occurs within the one-male groups of the hamadryas baboons studied by Kummer and Kurt.[14] These consist of two or more females grouped round a single adult male. The identity of these groups remains distinct even when a number of them associate together as a troop. Kummer has pointed out that they maintain their discrete coherence during the proximity of one-male groups to one another. In addition, Kummer and Kurt have evidence that the attention of the females is restricted almost exclusively to their own male, as can be seen from the fact that they follow the male as soon as he moves off; and, moreover, their interaction with near-by individuals from other groups is very small.

The recognition of the predominant direction of attention during distinct periods of activity of a group can reveal the structure of the relationships within that group. For example, in the usual foraging behaviour of a patas group consisting of female assemblies separated by a great distance from their attendant males, the predominant attention of the mother and young is directed towards each other in ways that have not yet been fully described, whereas that of the male is directed predominantly outwards towards the environment. The bachelor bands probably have a separate centre of attention within the band if they are found to be rank-ordered. In a savannah baboon group, on the other hand, all the individuals show predominant attention to the dominant males. A large environmentally directed component is also present in most of the adults, especially in the sub-dominant males, whose activity keeps them on the periphery of the group.

It is here suggested that in these situations the attention has a binding quality. If this is so, the amount of attention directed within the group is of paramount importance for an understanding of the inter-individual bond and of social organization. The relationship between individuals can then be understood by the way they orient themselves, both spatially and in dependent types of behaviour, with respect to the predominant focus of attention.

Broadly speaking, dominance is at present considered to be that attribute of an animal's behaviour which enables it to obtain an object when in competition with others. The means by which this is achieved is usually regarded as superior strength, whether exerted in direct competition by active threats or by persistent self-assertive bearing accompanied by a complete lack of hesitancy which brooks no delay in the response of its subordinates. This is sometimes accompanied by the suggestion that the recognition of superior strength by subordinates may be the result of prior experience or learning. There is little direct evidence and much supposition in this popular formulation and it is important to examine more closely the actual nature of dominance-submission relationships. A redefinition is now proposed on the assumption that the attention-binding effect of an animal in a group, not simply aggressiveness, is the essential quality which puts it in a behaviourally focal position and which also tends to place it near the group's spatial centre. Thus the dominant animal may be said to dominate the attention of others at most, if not all, times, and usually without taking any specific actions to achieve this.

This definition satisfies a feature of the dominance-submission relationship for which there has recently been increasing evidence: namely, that in many species the most active part of this relationship is played by the subordinate rather than by the dominant animal itself. This is consistent with a relationship based on the attention of the subordinate being constantly directed towards the dominant animal. Thus we should seek to define the nature of attention by the characteristics of the subordinate's behaviour, and investigate how its operation may be recognized and possibly measured, and what are its components and effects.

Social bonds : the outcome of predominant attention

Attention in primates is primarily one of visual awareness or, more precisely, awareness dependent on visual information. If an animal's attention is persistently drawn by another individual it needs to be informed as to where this dominant animal is at any particular moment. This can come about by scanning the whole field of vision until the position of the dominant animal is found, or by a simple turning movement oriented towards where he last was, implying some trace of awareness as a directing component. A recurrent, if sporadic, re-awakening of such memory traces would appear to act as reminders prompting the female gelada baboon to keep near her overlord despite the distractions of the other members of the troop. Likewise, the same type of promptings could account for the capricious behaviour of the male towards a wayward female.

The memory of where the dominant animal was may receive constant reinforcement by repeated glances towards, or seeking out of, the dominant individual. By this method a subordinate animal achieves reassurance that no change has taken place since the occasion when the dominant animal was last seen. The frequency with which this seeking out takes place depends on the urgency with which the subordinate animal needs this information, and this urgency will vary with the nature of the response which it is required to make. Hence, attention can be the result of previous aggression.

If all that it needs to do is to keep the dominant animal in sight in order to be able to follow it, then there will be no great urgency; but if, at the same time, it needs to avoid coming too close, or to keep an appropriate distance, the urgency will be greater. Finally, the greater the amount of movement among members of the group, the more attention will have to be directed away from other occupations in order to maintain or re-establish contact, or ensure the maintenance of a clear social space around dominant individuals.

To return to the behaviour of the dominant animal with this in mind, we can now see that an aggressive disposition in a dominant animal will engender a more urgent state in a subordinate one, and that the more specifically this aggression is directed at one individual the more it will tend to bind this individual's attention exclusively and thereby segregate this individual from the rest of the group and bind the relationship.

Persistent attention by subordinate members of a rank order towards more dominant members, or towards a supremely dominant individual, is a feature common to all the examples of rank-ordered behaviour reported. It is the mechanism whereby sentinel savannah baboons take up their position at the edge of a troop, as well as being the way in which members of the breeding hierarchy relate themselves to one another in this species. It is the way in which the initiative of the younger male macaques who move away from the night resting-places eventually becomes dependent on the movement of one of the dominant males at the centre, and this determines the movement of the group as a whole. It accounts for the cohesion and separate existence of male cohorts of chimpanzees, the breeding males of the Japanese and bonnet macaques, and the cohesiveness of gorilla bands and the 'leadership' of the dominant male gorilla. It appears to be the basis of the one-male group of the hamadryas baboon. Rank order and the cohesiveness of a cohort, band or heterosexual group therefore arise out of the persistent attention of subordinate towards the more dominant individuals of the group which, since it is directed ultimately at a single dominant individual, tends to space out the members of a rank order around this individual. It organizes behaviour along vectors radiating outwards from him when aggression is a prominent feature, and inwards towards him when subordinate behaviour is involved. Priority of access is not therefore a constant correlate of rank order relations within a group, nor is aggression always associated with high status. Hence, neither can be considered as a fundamental part of rank order relations. On the other hand, spatial features are the outcome of subordinate behaviour and attention to the dominant animal.

The societies which are organized during the active phases, and especially during agonistic periods, of their daily life cycle of activity together with, or around, a rank order of adult males can be described as centripetal. The centripetal attention of subordinates, balanced by escape from the dominant individual, tends to space them out around the dominant individual, usually a male, except when other activities disrupt this tendency.

We can now see that predominant attention to a single individual can, by acting as a common focus of attention, provide a means by which a number of individuals cohere; the same end can be achieved by a series of links in a chain of attention. It seems that a gorilla group, the members of which, as Schaller[15] says, are attentive to the movement of others in the dense forest environment, coheres by the latter means, except on the occasions when the dominant male stands motionless, with legs spread, indicating his readiness to move: then he becomes the focus of attention. The same occurs when he beats his chest.

In a baboon or macaque group, agonistic behaviour can include not only aggression and escape, but also mating. We can now see that in a state of high agonistic arousal each member of a group is likely to be kept close to the other by activation of the components of the SIAM complex, plus reflected escape. From the evidence of the animal's overt behaviour we see that the arousal of these drives may be the mechanism by which centripetal attention is engendered. The mechanisms controlling attention in them, therefore, reside at least partly in the intrinsic structure of the individual's behaviour, as well as in those outside signals which may demand attention.

The structure of attention is, then, the pattern represented by periods of continuous or oscillatory attention which link the individual's internal state of preparedness for social action to the members of the group or sub-group to which it belongs. The individual's attention structure thereby links it to its place in the society.

The nature of attention organized in the agonistic and hedonic modes

Virgo and Waterhouse[16] found a way of assessing the emergence of attention structure amongst rhesus macaques in the Bristol Zoo. They appear to have shown that in this colony, grooming relations constituted a network of 'positive' attention focused on an adult male, whereas subordination and avoidance responses were focused on an aggressive female, and they suggest that 'any theory of attention must take into account the possibility of divided foci of attention'. Reynolds and Luscombe[17] have studied the behaviour of a group of chimpanzees in a thirty-acre enclosure at the Holloman Air Force Base in the New Mexican desert, and they found that chimpanzee attention structure is based upon attention-demanding behaviour or display, practised competitively between males of the colony, and is distinct from the pattern of aggression between the same individuals. This display behaviour leads not to submission or appeasement by a subordinate, but is a form of social solicitation, as it leads on to forms of associative behaviour in which there is a continuing interaction between individuals, such as grooming, play, sexual or mothering behaviour with the displayer. That the rank order established by attention-demanding displays is directly comparable with other forms of rank order is evident from the fact that priority of access to preferred food is obtained by status in this rank order, showing that competitive success is not, in this instance, based on aggression. Aggression has to be opposed by counter-aggression, appeased, or avoided, all forms of behaviour designed to eliminate the intensity and continuity of the social contact. Display behaviour, responded to by greeting, stimulates and enhances the tendency of individuals to develop many forms of contact behaviour or behaviour at close quarters. Manipulation, both of the individual's own body or that of a companion, not only by grooming but also by holding and investigation, is jointly engaged in. Their attention may also switch to the environment or to other objects and give rise to manipulation of objects as tools.

Play which involves grappling the other individual can also be readily transferred to ropes, branches and loose branches or sticks, and then these physical objects used, as with sticks as scrapers or for poking, or as a means of display, or spectacularly, as in agile man-oeuvres such as pole vaulting, when a branch may be used to jump three times the height of the individual. Such varied and flexible behaviour, both social and non-social in form, but often involving the combined attention of two companions towards each other and towards a physical object, is clearly of a different nature from the rigid, fixed pattern of agonistic behaviour, and should be regarded as constituting a separate mode for which the term *hedonic* is proposed. This word has the same root as hedonism, but as yet has no specific correlation with the description of human behaviour, as has hedonistic. It is proposed that it should be taken into use as a classificatory term for the behaviour of subhuman primates, without the subjective connotation associated with 'hedonistic' but suggesting an affinity with pleasant human feelings.

From observation of this behaviour in two captive colonies of chimpanzees (at the Holloman Air Force Base and at the Delta Regional Primate Center, Covington, Louisiana) the following features suggest that the major difference that exists between the agonistic and hedonic modes of behaviour is as follows. In the hedonic mode, display leads to ongoing but flexible social relations which can act as the medium for the dissemination of information within the society. The processes underlying this dissemination of information may turn out to rely on actions which arise from the individual's propensities and others' reactions to these more than in the agonistic mode.

In the agonistic mode, information transfer from one individual to another is disrupted by responses to aggression: e.g. by inflexible rank-ordered social relations, by 'cut-off' acts and postures, and by gross differences in the way members of the society handle information (because of their social position).

It is further suggested that an individual's social attention in the hedonic mode is polydiadic: i.e. at any moment it relates one individual to another, but frequent changes of attention to other individuals are possible; whereas in the agonistic mode, which is essentially rank-ordered and centripetal, triadic relations occur, and often remain fixed, being part of the mechanism which coerces individuals to cohere in fixed rank-ordered social relations.

Organizational differences between species: acentric and centripetal societies

Four species, the patas, langur, gibbon and hamadryas baboon, differ from the rest of the species studied so far. In various ways the hetero-sexual groups of these species are organized round one male.

The patas, langur and gibbon are organized so as to take advantage of the refuge potential of the environment and are escape oriented towards it. Where a female assembly is present as in the langur, and especially in the patas, there is a tendency in agonistic behaviour (moderately developed in the langur and highly developed in the patas) for the female assemblies to separate from the attendant male. This characteristic separation of females from the males, because it disperses the components of the society, labels them as *acentric* societies (see Figures 11, 12 and 13).

The rest of the species studied so far are organized with, or around, a rank order of adult males. The societies centred on this rigidly organized sub-group cohere by a rank-ordered attention structure and, as we have said, can briefly be referred to as *centripetal* societies. Acentric societies are organized in a number of different ways, but they all differ from centripetal societies in lacking the continuous centripetal attention structure upon which the cohesion of all the components (female assemblies, male cohorts and juvenile clusters) depends.

We should note the differences within the various acentric societies. The gibbon has no more than one adult member of each sex in the group, and in the hamadryas the one-male groups keep apart during most of the active phase, though even in this society the start of the troop movements shows a residue of the influence of male centri-petal organization. As pointed out in the section on the langur, there is too little information about the bonds uniting the female assemblies and the males of this species. There is evidence in both the ontogeny and adult life of the langur of a residual bond, but when agonistic behaviour develops between males the females move away, indicating that the centripetal bonds are not highly developed in the females. The reverse is true of the behaviour of the centripetally organized savannah baboons; here the females become actively involved in the agonistic encounters. The looser association of the langur may well

SLEEPING

bachelor band

FORAGING

DIVERSIONARY ESCAPE

PREDATOR

crouching in long grass

leaping display

♂ = adult male		♂ = subadult male	
♀ = adult female		J = juvenile	
♂ = dominant male		Y = infant	

FIGURE 11: Patterns of aggregation and dispersal in an acentric society – patas monkey, *Erythrocebus patas*

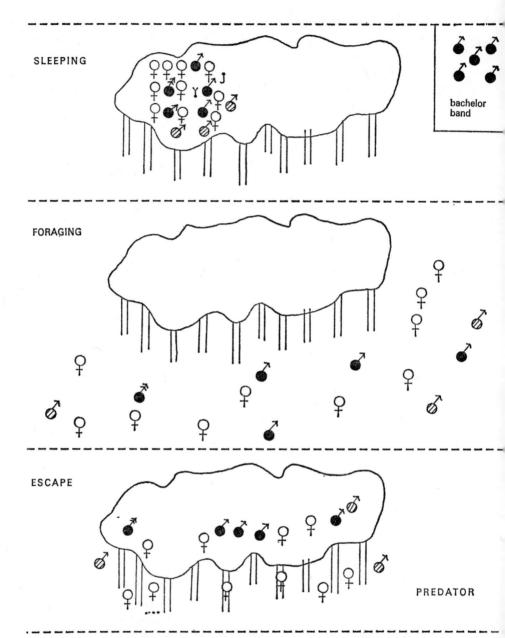

FIGURE 12: Patterns of aggregation and dispersal in a society showing both acentric and centripetal tendencies – langurs, *Presbytes entellus*

SLEEPING

cliff ledge;
single tree or
prominent rock

bachelor
(band ?)

FORAGING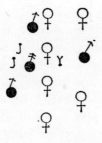

$\longrightarrow$

DEFENCE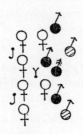

PREDATOR

 = adult male
♀ = adult female
 = dominant male

= subadult male
ʃ = juvenile
Y = infant

FIGURE 13: Patterns of aggregation and dispersal in a centripetal society – savannah
baboons, *Papio cynocephalus*

181

reflect the operation of a different defence system from that practised by the savannah baboons, which retreat as a group to a tree: the members of a langur group retreat individually to the protection of the forest trees where they are reassembled by the shaking of branches and calls of the males bouncing about in the tree tops. There is less cohesiveness in the langur when excited because the individual drive structure possesses a larger proportion of intra-specific escape-arousal compared with the other aspect of flight motivation, social sub-mission. Attention to the features of the physical environment in preference to attention towards other members of the group, and especially a dominant individual, go together with intra-specific escape tendencies, causing dispersion of the group when under attack by predators. The absence of any mention in the literature of specific submission gestures confirms this. Jay's[18] insistence on avoidance or spatial equilibrium or, as she says, 'personal space', probably also reflects this feature, as does the use of the active type of agonistic gesture, such as lunge, hit, slap, bite and wrestle, which indicates that the aggressor must rely on active deflection of an opponent's attention rather than being able to solicit submission by threat towards a subordinate already attentive towards a more dominant individual, as in the savannah baboon. The langur society may therefore be said to be biased more towards the female assemblies with a larger escape component to the individual's motivation, enabling each individual to orient towards aspects of the physical environment when in danger.

If this can be seen to be so for the langur's behaviour, the escape component in the behaviour of the patas is not only more evident, but is predominant in both the behaviour of the crouching female assemblies and the distraction displays of the adult male, who keeps his distance from the females during the active part of the daily cycle. The attention of the male patas is oriented spatially with respect to the predator, the physical surroundings and the location of the female assemblies, but only so as to put as much distance as possible between the females and himself, so that when they are surprised by a predator the females can hide without being noticed, or they can all escape together as fast as possible.

As explained in the previous chapter, erratic components of pro-tean behaviour such as bouncing are part of escape. When erratic components appear in agonistic behaviour this is evidence that they are readily available in the repertoire and therefore that a large proportion of escape is present in the agonistic motivation. The predominant escape component of the individual patas's motivation structure is further evidenced in the active forms of aggression which are themselves erratic: these involve sudden attacks to which escape is the immediate response, there being no sustained balanced agonism but sudden sharp oscillation between agonism and escape – hence the absence of agonistic sexual presentation.

Finally, the appearance of bouncing – during invitation to play, when pouncing on food, during the diversionary display of the male, during escape running of all individuals and as part of the pouncing attacks of one female on another – shows the widespread occurrence of an escape component, determining the form of much high arousal activity. This society can therefore be said to be organized by being predominantly escape motivated into adult sub-groups which are widely separated. Little more is known about the way in which the majority of adult males live than the existence of male bands.

The structure of attention in the society of the langur and, to a much greater extent, of the society of the patas monkey is arranged so as to enable escape to be organized in relation to the physical environment. The escape of the langur is therefore not capable of being reflected back towards the centre of the society, but is directed away from other individuals; this enables sufficient attention to be paid to the environment to assist the individual's escape. This is the characteristic of acentric societies. To enable the behaviour to be so organized a large escape motivation is required in the individual. In general, submission is absent, as also is its counterpart, high level threat, and erratic elements are seen to be widespread throughout many other types of behaviour.

Let us now assess the significance of the classification of societies into centripetal and acentric types. At first sight it might appear better to classify the centripetal societies as centric societies and the others as acentric; that is to say, societies possessing a centre and those without one. But by calling the societies centripetal we draw attention to the fact that it is the organization of the individual's attention within the group that is critical. We refer to the fact that in the centripetal societies the lives of the individuals are all the time organized with reference to its attention to the dominant animal, and especially that the escape tendency is reflected back towards the dominant centre of the group. In terms of attention structure this really means that when the individual is escape motivated, as well as when motivated by positive social tendencies, its attention remains on the same focus – the centre of the group or the dominant individual at that centre. Hence throughout all forms of activity it has a single centre of attention, whereas (as illustrated by the patas monkey, which under attack by predators organizes its behaviour on the physical environment) there is in the behaviour of the individuals of an acentric society a sudden switch of the underlying orientation of attention towards another feature of the environment and away from a social centre about which are organized all the social relationships of that individual. Hence in acentric societies there is a disruption of attention at times of high excitement, whereas in centripetal societies this is not so.

Hans Kummer[19] has recently assessed the optimum distances which separate different classes of individual hamadryas baboon, and finds that a time sample shows a distribution curve with a mode at a short distance apart for females and a wider one for males, indicating, as he says, a balance between attractive and repellent influences. Making the same assessment of the distance separating two patas males at a later date in the same enclosure he found no smooth curve, but a greater frequency, forming peaks in the curve representing the fact that the individuals could not move about the enclosure without attempting to keep near significant objects as well as maintaining distance from the companion. This shows that their behaviour was controlled by both social influences and significant features of the physical environment. This confirms the deduction that an acentric form of attention governs social behaviour in the patas monkey.

It was suggested earlier in the chapter that intra-specific escape tendencies are engendered by predatory attacks on the society. We can see that this is confirmed by the fact that individuals in a centripetal society do not exhibit, as do individuals in an acentric society like that of the patas, the forms of behaviour typical of escape motivation; so it may be that a continuous centripetally organized attention also involves the suppression of actual escape motivation, and that this may be the most significant feature of a centripetally organized society. If so, the disruptive elements of protean behaviour so characteristic of escape motivated individuals are eliminated from the organization of their social repertoire.

The societies of the savannah baboons and the patas monkey therefore stand at opposite poles, but both are organized for defence in open country: the one centripetally, using aggression, the other acentrically, by distraction displays by the male combined with escape immobility of the female assembly. How is it, then, since they both occupy the same kind of territory and, indeed, their ranges overlap in the savannah areas south of the Sahara Desert, that they have developed such different means of survival? One clue may be in their feeding habits. Often the baboon searches in the open for food, much of which is just below the surface of the ground and requires powerful digging to unearth, whereas the patas roams continually, gathering and catching as it goes food which is all readily available without the exertion of much physical force. Hence the baboon requires a stocky physique with powerful arms and legs, and has not developed the long, lanky limbs required for successful escape in rapid flight. It might be thought that these basic differences were the responses to danger and feeding requirements acting as constraining factors in the evolution of the social propensities which distinguish the two different societies. But the factor initiating the divergent evolutionary trends was the behavioural difference in the methods of searching for food in the different species. Given these basic differences the divergent modalities of behaviour follow. Hence we see an interaction between the requirements of feeding and defence determining the social form by contributing to the evolution of specific motivational patterns in the individual.

Whether or not similarities between the repertoire of two different species are evidence of a common origin can only be decided on the basis of some other information on whether the similarity could be due to convergent evolution. The structure of the behavioural repertoire must be known, however, not only before any assessment of evolutionary origin is possible, but even to enable similarities of repertoire to be recognized and a proper comparison made. Thus the fact that the bonnet macaque at a high level of arousal crouches to neck-bite, and possesses a presentation gesture which is also exercised outside agonistic situations, suggests an affinity of repertoire with the hamadryas and gelada which requires investigation, and may also go some way towards explaining why damaging fights break out between the rank order males of these species.

Once we understand what is meant by the structure of an individual's repertoire we are able to see that the behaviour of the patas monkey is escape motivated in readiness for the presence of a predator; this is partly responsible for the distribution of the individuals in a range (involving the separation of the males into cohorts and one-male groups with females), which reduces the occasions on which agonistic encounters between males of the community take place. Therefore these monkeys do not require a social submission pathway and do not possess a submission posture.

On the other hand, agonistic encounters are very frequent in centripetal societies such as those of baboons and macaques in which presentation inhibits aggression as well as functioning as a mating invitation. Nevertheless, Wickler,[20] who has systematized the evidence, does not dissociate the aggression-suppression component from the apparent sexual element. This is because ever since Zuckerman[21] formulated his sexual attractiveness hypothesis to explain primate sociability, sexuality has been considered by most primatologists to be a *sine qua non* of sociability in primates.

The argument for or against the hypothesis put forward by Zuckerman can anyhow be seen as irrelevant because it is couched in terms of reproductive physiology rather than in terms of behaviour structure. It can be seen that in the structure of behaviour an agonistic blocked escape pathway of response is merged with a sexual one in the centripetal primates, and the conflict is resolved in this way. In the patas, on the other hand, there is no conflict to be resolved because the individuals are widely spaced out and the sexes are separate. This is the single species in which mating behaviour plays no part in sociability, yet it is able to mate.

It can be noted that species which possess an agonistic centripetal social structure also possess red skin patterns: those that walk on all fours, such as the rhesus and baboon, on hocks, rump and face; those that sit, such as the gelada, on the chest and face, these being the postures most of them adopt in agonistic social situations. Whereas in the gelada both sexes have red patches on the chest, as they sit for so much of the time, Wickler notes that the males do not possess 'carunculations of the skin along the border of the chest patch' (and seem to display only one of the two colour phases seen in the female). Presumably this is because the red skin is required in agonistic situations equally by both sexes, the colour on the chest and face acting as a sign-suppressor of threat in the case of the seated gelada baboon, as does the colour on the face, rump and hocks of the presenting macaque and hamadryas baboon. The effectiveness of the signal may well be enhanced by being located next to the sexual swellings of the female, so increasing visibility by contrast with the red colour itself during the receptive period. It is not in itself a specific sexual signal,* as is the highly light-reflective distance signal of the female's turgid sexual skin. (The latter, as Herbert[22] of Birmingham has shown, also emits a sexually attractive smell.)

The red colouration is not only a signal suppressing threat by the attacker; it can be deduced that it will also serve as a signal to ward off approach, and in this conflict, therefore, mating is only possible when an additional attractive signal is given by the female. The patas, which does not present and is not warding off any approach, may be sexually attractive in an unknown way which is freely responded to. Centripetal societies of the macaques and baboons rely for safety on cohesion around well-armed males which are also well primed with a strong predisposition towards aggression. This is directed mostly within the society and therefore social relations are a source of much conflict. Various devices are present in the behaviour to minimize the effects of the tendency towards aggression. The essential foundations are a submission posture (according to Virgo and Waterhouse captive rhesus colonies show more than one submission posture) and reflected escape tendencies at high levels of arousal.

The behaviour of adults in centripetal societies, as we have seen, is organized round the propensity of individuals to cluster about the dominant male, and therefore it involves raising the arousal state of the females towards that of the males so that the same tendencies operate in both. At the same time, this subjects them to the hazards

* Since this deduction was made J. Herbert[23] has found that the red colouration of the rhesus, unlike the white sexual swelling, does not respond to sex hormones. This is consistent with the suggestion that the red colouration itself does not act as a specifically sexual signal.

of male aggression, so it might be reasonable to expect that this type of bond cementing the female assemblies to the male cohorts might be supplemented by bonds less provocative of conflict. It is probably significant, therefore, that in the societies of many of these centripetal species with strong aggressive features, the males show interest in the young and thereby create a bond which does little to cause conflict between the sexes. Savannah baboon males take an interest in the young from the day they are born. The hamadryas male kidnaps youngsters and eventually adopts a young female, cementing this relationship by an agonistic bond which incorporates her into his harem. The bonnet macaque male plays with infants and young, and Japanese macaque males mother one-year-old infants when they are free of the mother. Of the species with centripetal societies, only the male rhesus appears to be relatively indifferent. By contrast, it is worth noting that male interest in the young is absent in the males of the langur, gelada and patas monkey. As a special feature, the young possess dark markings, ensuring freedom from attack; consequently they have the possibility of greater movement throughout the society and hence are able to establish contacts which give them sources of support other than their mothers.

It is not difficult to see that the overriding feature to which any society has to be adapted is the requirement of survival from attack by predators, where these are a real threat to their existence. The argument put forward in this chapter has attempted to show that the mode through which this survival is achieved has profound consequences for the nature of the society, and largely determines its internal structure as well as the way it meets attack from outside. Two modes, defence and protection, organized from the centre of the group, and escape, taking advantage of local environmental features, bring about differences in the spatial organization of subgroups which are essentially the outcome of the structure of the individual's social repertoire. This not only acts to provide it with the appropriate defensive or evasive tactics but also largely determines how much of the rest of the social life shall be carried on.

In the societies of both the chimpanzee and the gorilla, which are also centripetally organized, there is, however, little agonism in the social relations. Chimpanzee males play with and are tolerant of their young, and the adult male gorilla is largely indifferent to the antics of the young which play on and around them. The centripetal organization of the great apes, therefore, seems to keep together a group of individuals which interfere less with each other's life than do members of the centripetal cercopithecoid monkeys studied. Kortlandt's and the Reynoldses' discovery that the chimpanzee takes the initiative in harassing potential predators, and the size of the gorilla itself, may be factors responsible for reducing the occasions on which both species find defence in an emergency necessary, and hence may leave these species free of the persistent propensity to agonistic behaviour.

To summarize, therefore, what this chapter has proposed: Acentric societies are those in which each individual's attention switches under predatory attack so that the organization of its behaviour is no longer oriented towards the rest of the society, but suddenly each individual looks to the features of the physical environment as the spatially significant aspect of the environment towards which to organize its response to the predator. This means that the coherence of the group is lost, and the sudden switch of the individual's attention from social orientation towards physical objects requires a new principle of orientation. Behaviour with reference to these two aspects of the environment may therefore represent two basically distinct modes of organization.

Centripetal societies, as we have seen, are typical both of species which possess a high level of aggressivity (such as the baboons and macaques), and of the great apes, in which aggressivity is low. In societies where it is high, threat and counter-threat are likely forms of agonistic behaviour between individuals, and, as we have seen, when one monkey or baboon uses protected threat he places himself in the direct line between his opponent and the dominant male, thereby not only enabling himself to solicit the dominant male's own threats towards his opponent, but placing the opponent at the disadvantage that if he counter-threatens he may inadvertently threaten the dominant male and so precipitate severe retaliation. Thus the aggressor involves the dominant male not only as an inadvertent protector but also as a potential aggressor. The equilibratory and submissive behaviour adopted by other animals towards the dominant individual indicates that an attack by him is the most important event to be avoided. Thus in spatial terms each individual must place himself on a separate radius with respect to the dominant individual in order to avoid inadvertent threats at him during the many agonistic encounters in which the individuals are involved. Hence there is a tendency for a wheel-like spatial organization to develop in agonistic centripetal societies operating in the open. This is clearly less likely to develop in non-agonistic centripetal societies, and we have indeed seen that the societies of chimpanzees and gorillas do not show the same clumping as baboons and macaques in the open. While some effects of interference by features of the physical environment may be responsible for the stepwise attention structure in gorilla society, it is highly significant that when chimpanzees move into the open they do so in a line, with a linear arrangement of cohort males in the centre of the group as it moves from one part of the country to another.

In all centripetal societies, however, attention towards a dominant individual is liable to develop, and although the mobbing of model leopards by chimpanzees has not been studied with a view to noting the role this type of organization plays, all the individuals co-ordinate in their attacks with other individuals and retreat into a clump when not in the actual attack. Centripetal spatial organization is, therefore, at the root of subhuman primate groups which cohere throughout their lives.

CHAPTER SEVEN

Movement Within the Society

Arousal and activity

In the last chapter we outlined a static picture of the societies, and in order to complete it we should consider some of the processes which, on the one hand, underlie the individual's ability to change its behaviour, and, on the other, are responsible for the way in which the individual moves from one sub-group to another.

In identifying the main sub-groups in the stem structure of the societies we have seen clearly for the first time that in acentric societies the males are kept separate from the females, whereas in the societies with centripetal tendencies the sexes are brought together. In the cercopithecoid species studied the males possess moderate to high-level aggression. The females, juveniles and young of centripetal societies have to adapt to this, whereas when they are kept separate they do not. In a langur society, which may be regarded as somewhat intermediate between an acentric and a centripetal society, the females move away as soon as fighting starts between adult and subadult males. But in societies in which the sexes cohere, the females make the adjustment either by submission postures or by spatial adjustment (equilibration) and counter-threat, all elements of a balanced agonistic state. The control of this social excitement is of importance not only for the stability of the society, but also for the adjustment of the individual's behaviour within it. Hence it seems important to recognize what form these adjustments take. In savannah baboon society the frequent high level of social excitement brings about, by reflected escape, the cohesion of those involved. An interest in the youngsters shown by all the adult males would therefore seem superfluous for linking the members of the society together, but undoubtedly it provides an alternative bond which could come into operation at times of less marked excitement and so keep the females with infants close to the centre and fully protected at most times. It is important, therefore, as a means of defining the links between the major sub-groups, to know something of how individuals may move from one part of the society to another.

An appropriate way to start thinking about this is to use as an example the behaviour of the infant as it clings to its mother, as discussed in Chapter 4. The best-known study of this behaviour is by the two Harlows,[1] who showed that it is the opportunities offered by the mother for clinging which attract the young, and that sucking and holding the nipple in the mouth are secondary considerations, as also is the satisfaction of the food provided.

In 1939 McCulloch[2] set out to discover if clinging, for a young chimpanzee, was a reward in delayed response tasks and discrimination performance. Naturally enough, he also found that after the young chimpanzee had been allowed to cling to some object, its motivation for clinging was temporarily reduced. Only as an incidental observation did he note that this appeared to be so only if the young chimpanzee was 'disturbed' or 'excited', but William Mason,[3] who took up the matter again in the 1960s, started with no bias concerning the processes underlying the phenomenon and recorded the occasions on which the young chimpanzees had been seen to cling to their mother. The literature provided evidence that this happened
1. in fights among and between groups,
2. when the group entered strange territory,
3. when predators were present, or
4. after the infant had been left a long way behind, or when, in captivity, the mother and infant had been artificially separated for some time.

Mason, studying chimpanzees in captivity, found that the young were prompted to cling to their mother by strange surroundings, physical restraint by the operator, separation from their mother and by loud noises. He therefore postulated that since a wide range of stimuli could bring about this clinging response, the infants were 'emotionally aroused' by all these conditions.

It might be thought likely, from the way the mother behaves towards the clinging infant, that cradling or hugging by the mother would reduce the tendency to cling, but curiously enough this has not been investigated. Since this action, by reducing the need to cling, automatically reduces the tension of the infant's muscles, it is also likely to reduce the infant's arousal. Juvenile savannah baboons and rhesus monkeys hug each other during excited moments of play and when general social disturbances cause them to be excited, and they may be rewarded by a relaxation of tension. Indeed, capture of his prospective female consort by the young hamadryas male, since this involves hugging the female infant, may be responsible for her becoming attached to him. Similar behaviour has been noted in young macaque males towards infants discarded by their mothers at the time of the next breeding season, and these males set up short-lived attachments to these infants.

The next stage in Mason's complex investigation showed that in unfamiliar situations a young chimpanzee would prefer to cling to a surrogate mother rather than to 'escape'. By this he means escape from the enclosure in which he observed the young chimpanzee, but, as we have already seen, a chimpanzee does not escape from an enclosure but is only endowed with the faculty of escaping towards a mother or mother substitute. The consummation of escape for a chimpanzee is clinging to a suitable parental object, and this is presumably why it so effectively reduces the desire to cling, and screaming in response to noxious stimuli did not take place when the animal was allowed to cling.

The form in which clinging takes place has all the characteristics of a consummatory act. It is relatively resistant to alterations by experience and is easily recognizable under widely different sets of conditions. It is, for example, easily recognized whether it is directed towards an inanimate object, the animal's own body, a person or another chimpanzee. The essential features of bi-manual grasping with both arms and hands and ventral contact are present in every case.

It is therefore clear that it is the activity which is consummatory, rather than the situation or object to which it is directed.

Emil Menzel[4] is not quite so sure that the situation is of no importance; possibly this is because most of his investigations are less structured and less designed to test specific hypotheses, and because he realizes that in a diverse environment more of the total structure is visible. His observations show that a location is as often a refuge or source of reassurance as is a companion. As he says, probably trees, corners, walls and fences can serve in this way.

> Nearly all chimps tend to remain close to them (especially if they are familiar) even when with companions. If upset or startled, the chimp will run preferably to a companion, but often simply to a vertical structure: and if the occasion is really severe, two animals will first grab each other and then move to a preferred tree, corner, etc. Most prolonged social clinging, in fact, occurs at such places, as does the self-directed or autistic behavior of isolation-raised chimps and clinging to blankets, etc. If a socially raised chimp is separated from his companions, he sticks closer than ever to familiar areas, verticals, etc. He does not often cling to trees or fences in exactly the same fashion that he clings to a companion, but the response patterns do include proximity seeking and (frequently) ventral contact and clasping or closure of the hand round the object; and screaming and other signs of upset are decreased as the object is approached and contacted ... at the same time there can be fairly pronounced preference among the objects; e.g. a young chimp tends to sleep in or retreat to the same corner of a room.[4]

Mason now investigated the relationship of this behaviour to a number of other components which are associated with the movement of the young chimpanzee away from these locations or objects of reassurance. He noted that, following a period of separation, cage-mates display a sequence of activities which characteristically starts with clinging, is followed by grooming and finally by play.

He therefore postulates that what happens when the young chimpanzee clings to its mother or an object is not the reduction of escape-arousal so much as a reduction to a lower overall level of arousal at which first of all grooming and then play, at a still lower level of arousal, come into operation, and that the activities themselves are responsible for bringing about this overall reduction of arousal. This is an attractive hypothesis, which as we shall see has been suggested by Andrew[5] to account for changes in the vocalization of sub-human primates, which will be discussed farther on.

In experiments in which he provided various forms of social

stimulation preceding a period of observation, Mason found that clinging was least following a calming stimulus, whereas the amount of play became high, but that following social play or other arousing stimuli playing was much reduced and clinging increased. This means that play and clinging have opposite effects on arousal; the more clinging, the less playing, and vice versa. Play would be expected to heighten arousal because of the frequent changes in the patterns of stimulation, and a rise in arousal can be inferred because it sometimes gives rise to fighting.

As we shall see later on, other features of the stimulus, such as contrast, may play a part. The differences between the concept of arousal and that of drive is that the intensity of arousal is non-specific, so that any stimulus which produces any given level of arousal will evoke a predisposition to behave in a particular way. Thus many variables, including intense auditory stimulation, separation from a cage-mate, strange surroundings, physical restraint and novel social stimuli, may have equivalent effects on social responsiveness, suggesting that a common mechanism is operative, not closely linked to specific types of stimulus.

The non-specificity of the stimulus, combined with the predisposition to act in a particular way at any given level of arousal, accounts not only for spontaneity, but also for the deployment of a normally socially-oriented type of behaviour towards a physical object.

In the social environment all types of activities are shown, so that cycles of activity occur in which play (which increases arousal) leads to grooming and clinging, both of which reduce arousal. In this cycle of activities the control of arousal is the central feature and gives an explanation of the structure of juvenile play as a way of teaching the maturing animal to control its behaviour in the social environment.

Arousal and primate calls and sounds

The concept arrived at by Mason – that certain sets of acts reflect a definite level of arousal – is the way Andrew explained vocalization in the primates.

Instead of using certain functional categories such as 'warning calls' and 'threat calls' he classifies the calls by using an audiographic analysis of the sounds, and finds that there are five different types which can be arranged on an intensity scale. He then lists the situations in which each type is found, and so has a more logical way of classifying the evocative situations on an intensity scale. They are:

1. The lowest occurred when perceiving a desired object.
2. (a) Encountering a social fellow after a brief separation.
   (b) Infant searching for the nipple.
3. (a) Male approaching a female to attempt copulation.
   (b) Attempting to reach a desired object.
4. (a) Loss of contact with the group.
   (b) Attempts to reach a desired object.
5. (a) Chased or seized by a superior.
   (b) Loss of bodily contact with an infant.

Finally he suggested that an increasing amount of stimulus contrast brings about the graduated stages of arousal.

Graded stimulus contrast has been shown by psychologists like Berlyne[6] to be one of a number of stimulus components responsible for increasing arousal, and this can be the mechanism for the additive effects of diverse stimuli. For some systems, such as those described by Andrew, it provides an easily recognizable basis for differentiating stimuli, but specificity of stimuli has been demonstrated in a number of studies by ethologists in the analysis of social behaviour of other species of primate. This means that there is more than one arousal mechanism controlling social behaviour.

Arousal and direction of approach

It has been pointed out that in centripetal societies, like those of macaques and savannah baboons, threats arising from high-ranking males of the society paradoxically do not lead to a dispersion of the threatened individuals, except perhaps briefly, but are shortly followed by a movement of the threatened individuals towards the members at the top of the rank order, which we have already pointed out are the focus of persistent attention.

In Chapter 4 the paradox seemed to be accentuated by the fact that while this was still true of the young males' behaviour towards adult males, it did not follow threats from the mother at weaning, driving away the young from her. It was suggested that a major difference was that the males only threatened briefly, whereas the females kept up persistent and vigorous rebuttals of approaches by their young.

Mason[7] was the first to suggest a mechanism whereby the behaviour of animals in centripetal societies approaching a threatening animal could be explained. He noted that unfamiliar objects first caused withdrawal and later elicited strong approach, suggesting that these two responses are on a simple continuum of arousal, withdrawal taking place at high arousal and approach as arousal drops away. As he says, applying this line of reasoning to social stimuli, an animal that is frequently and openly aggressive will be less attractive than one that merely threatens and then desists. Since threats and aggressive displays are fairly common and 'full-blown' attacks rare, the cohesion of centripetal societies is maintained by frequent threats spaced out in time, which, after a delay when the initial high level of arousal has dissipated somewhat, brings about approach towards the dominant animals, which are not only the focus of persistent attention but maintain this state by well-timed threats.

The same arousal-control mechanism can be seen in operation when there is a different vectoral distribution of the components of the individual's agonistic social behaviour, as when chimpanzees harass leopards.

With mating and escape directed to companions (see Figure 10, p. 170), aggression is directed towards the model leopard in the first stages, when arousal (indicated by general excitement) is very high. Later, when things have quietened down, aggression is replaced by inquisitiveness and investigatory approaches to the model.

The vectoral distribution of components of social behaviour in operation between members of a chimpanzee group while harassing a leopard reinforces reassurance by switching mating and escape to companions, thus leaving investigation and aggression solely directed towards the model leopard. In this situation the tendency to escape is satisfied, and arousal lowered, reducing the value of repellent signals from the leopard; this facilitates approach to the leopard, first of all with aggression and then with investigation.

It is now possible to see how the major predispositions to act orient the behaviour and are defined in the behaviour by the structure of

197

the individual's social repertoire, increasing the awareness of significant stimuli. Differential approaches to the same object at different levels of arousal can now be seen to be the result of the use of different built-in tendencies.

An example of holding behaviour as the result of a switch in motivation is provided by the young chimpanzee which does not yet have an aggressive component, where we have seen that clinging arises in a high state of arousal, on return to the mother; the same is true of the young macaque or baboon. In the adult baboon or macaque this clinging is not retained at the end of reflected escape. If any form of contact takes place in the adult macaque it takes the form of grooming, often reflected on to the ground at the end of reflected escape. In the young chimpanzee, however, clinging to and grasping a familiar object becomes as reassuring as clinging to a companion and returning to a familiar place, and therefore holding an object can be initiated by one type of motivation and carried on by another at different levels of arousal. It clings to reassure itself at the high level of arousal and holds the same object in exploratory behaviour, which is an activity at a lower level of arousal. This may well be why attempting to reach a desired object is associated with cries indicative of the middle range of arousal in Andrew's scale, since the attempt to reach masks two forms of holding an object.

A chimpanzee carries an object around because it gets reassurance from it. Then, as soon as it has got reassurance, it can begin to manipulate it in exploratory behaviour or can learn to hold it and explore, as when it pushes it into a hole.

Returning to consider the vectorial organization of motive, we know that baboons and macaques will escape to the safety of trees or prominent outcrops of rock if in danger from attack. Where these are not available, the dominant male is the refuge, and escape becomes reflected back towards the social focus of attention. There are two distinct situations in which this will occur. We may first consider what happens because of the presence in centripetal societies of males possessing a high level of aggression: whenever a social disturbance occurs they are at its focus and are likely to threaten members of the society who, because of their tendency for reflected escape, keep close to them despite being attacked by them. In these circumstances the attention of the subordinates becomes focused on the centre, and since there is no other feature such as a predator on which to direct their attention, the individuals of the society become involved with each other: they are caught in fixed rituals of cut-off and displacement close to the dominant focus, or involved in various combinations of ganging up for attack on low-ranking individuals, protected threat, displaced attack on a scapegoat or stepwise redirection of attacks towards others of attacks made upon them.

All these forms, however, are centre-oriented and only secondarily become displaced outwards towards low-ranking individuals at the periphery of the society; these individuals are then able to reduce the intensity of agonistic involvement by temporarily widening the space between themselves and these others. Low-ranking individuals therefore act as an alternative focus of attention, and most of the members of the society who occupy positions of intermediate status then receive some reassurance from the fact that their rear is covered by the presence of the dominant male. They are free to direct their aggression elsewhere, as in protected threat.

This type of simple (vectoral) organization now becomes adopted by all members when a predator is present, the individual's tendency to escape still being satisfied at the centre of the society, and their aggression now focused, together with that of all the other individuals, on the predator. In this way the social relationships which otherwise would have been diversified and complex are now all of the same kind. Moreover, this is a situation, for the adults at least, of persistent high arousal since except for the mothers with their infants clinging to them, none of the adults are involved in contact reassurance while in danger. This is not so, however, for the adult chimpanzees mobbing a leopard; after making wild forward dashes at it, throwing sticks and beating at it with sticks, they return to hug, kiss, touch and mount other adults for reassurance, and this reduces arousal.

There is, however, a notable distinction between the baboons and macaques on the one hand and the chimpanzees on the other; while the cercopithecoid species seem to be always operating towards the predator under an ambivalent motivation, and also probably under the influence of aggression balanced by escape tendencies, the aggressive motivation of the chimpanzee is not interfered with by opposing tendencies. He is more single-minded. This becomes evident in the type of aggressive assault typical of each. The adult baboon will threaten and move towards the object of his aggression until in one dash he can rush forward and direct a blow. The chimpanzee's behaviour, on the other hand, is more correctly described as harassing, since wild leaps which distract the predator are interspersed with repeated blows directed at it, before the individual chimpanzee returns for reassurance. When the predator is dislodged or has gone away, chimpanzees are soon able to return to rest because of their immediate giving and acceptance of contact reassurance. Although baboons have not been observed in these circumstances, grooming takes a prominent place between pairs of individuals during agonistic episodes within the baboon groups. In a macaque colony, the Reynoldses observed that the higher the rank of a male individual the more that individual was involved in grooming, especially towards his female consort. Grooming also plays a large part in the post-agonistic episodes of the bonnet macaque. Grooming would therefore appear to be a transitional activity diverting attention away from agonistic activity and providing a ritualized form of contact behaviour which, though no real evidence has been sought on the subject, probably provides reassurance and reduces arousal.

Young chimpanzees have little aggression and so we are only able to see the interaction between escape and investigation or play, and they seem able to get reassurance both from inanimate objects like preferred trees to which they return, from companions or from objects to which they have become attached (a parallel to children and their toys). This tendency to escape to objects and companions is also present in the adult, and appears to represent the retention of an infantile trait into adult life; it is a feature the baboon or macaque does not possess. Kortlandt's[8] discovery that chimpanzees inhabit open forest where space and refuges provided by trees are intermingled, as well as dense forests, reveals how well adapted the chimpanzee is to its habitat – as well as is the baboon, whose behaviour is adapted to more open country.

CHAPTER EIGHT

The Form of Primate Primary Social Groups

Some of the conclusions that have emerged from this survey are new, and need to be reviewed against the background of existing ideas about various features of subhuman primate societies.

The terms centripetal and acentric have been used to distinguish two types of society in which the individual's social behaviour is organized in radically different ways. In order to comprehend the nature of the distinction one must realize that escape is escape whether it is directed away from a predator or away from a social companion, and that it is an integral part of the structure of the individual's social repertoire. This is so because only by modifying this aspect of an individual's relation to a companion is that individual's social capability enhanced, as was seen in the section on the comparative morphology of the individual's social repertoire. If this is accepted, then it is also possible to see that in a centripetal society there are no situations when the centre of that society is not the focus of attention for the individual; his behaviour is organized around it during all types of emotional arousal. In an acentric society, on the other hand, under predatory attack the individual loses his social orientation and escapes to the protection of the environment so that the society falls apart. In acentric societies the individual does not seek or receive protection from a social focus of attention, and as a result his escape tendency is no longer in balance with other social tendencies. Instead it takes over completely, temporarily eliminating his social awareness. This latter point brings into operation protean tendencies which, as far as adaptive considerations go, are not required in a centripetal society. Yet, as we have seen, this disruptive pattern will emerge whenever escape is intense. Important though this is, it is probably less so for the total integration of behaviour than is the fact that where a single focus exists in the social environment of an individual, all social capabilities are integrated under all states of excitement.

The distinction is clearest between the society of the patas monkey, as the most typical representative of an acentric society, and the societies of the savannah baboon, the macaques (rhesus, bonnet and Japanese) and the great apes – chimpanzees and gorillas – representing centripetal societies. The hamadryas possesses a centripetally organized one-male unit, but the heterosexual society as a whole is less clearly structured and is disrupted by the dispersion of the one-male unit during the daytime. The gelada presents much the same picture. Gibbon society, by its nature, is excluded from this classification and may be primitive. Of those reported, only the langur society appears to be intermediate, in that it can operate in either form when in danger.

The three components of the society – the female assemblies, the male cohorts and the juvenile clusters – present in the complex societies of monkeys and apes have distinct characteristics: that is to say the behaviour of the individuals in them takes on distinctive forms. The females in their assemblies are packed closer together than are the males in their cohorts. Hans Kummer[1] has demonstrated that this results from the tendency of males to maintain an optimum distance from each other which is different and larger than that of females from each other, so that although at any one moment one individual may be close to or far away from another there is an optimum distance at which individuals will be found more often than on other occasions.

In the female assemblies, contact behaviour plays a larger part than in the behaviour of members of male cohorts to one another, where it is largely absent, and aggression is expressed in female assemblies by hitting, snapping and biting rather than by threats and chases.

The origins of status

The rank-ordered relationships in both the female assemblies and the male cohorts plays a significant role in the wider relationships in a heterosexual society. The support a mother and her offspring will give to each other when attacked by a third party, as has been observed by Walter Angst[2] in his colony of *Macaca fascicularis* in the Basel Zoo, represents a continuous relationship between them. This arises out of the initial mother/child relationship, and is probably instrumental in imparting the dependent rank of the female to her offspring, as has been demonstrated in Japanese macaque societies. Clearly, therefore, rank in the society has its origin from within the female assemblies, where the dependent rank of the offspring is the point from where the infant is initiated into society. A young female may get most of his status from dependent rank, but the rank of an individual male arises from this status in the male cohort where it expresses more of his individual prowess, which he then imparts to his consort, at least for a while, during consort relations with her.

The determinants of behaviour of all kinds are always the inter-action between hereditary disposition and experience, the resultant behaviour becoming more or less fixed by learning. This may be accepted, but does not clarify the factors involved in establishing a rank order, or in what way these operate to produce the final result. This is partly because we are as yet unaware of how all the individuals in a group are ranked. The apparent restriction of the numbers of a cohort to six or seven in a heterosexual centripetal society may do no more than express the fixed relations at the top of a system of ranking which, at the lower end, consists of individuals equally fixed in their subordination. The difference between them lies in the way they behave; those at the top have a fuller repertoire of behaviour capable of maintaining social relations, while those at the bottom are more liable to rely on avoidance and escape. Whether or not learning brings about fixation in an individual's behaviour, and if so how, will be likely to depend on the distinctly different modalities within the individual's repertoire shown by any particular individual at a particular status in the rank order.

It has been shown that an important feature of rank-ordered behaviour is the way the subordinate individuals pay attention to those higher in rank, and a study of this feature should yield much more valuable information about the nature of rank order than a study concentrating only on competitive success or aggressive dominance. In any event, since aggression is evidently not a constant correlate of high status, it should no longer be considered either the most important aspect of a dominant individual's behaviour or the determinant of rank.

As we saw in Chapter 6, the work of Virgo and Waterhouse[3] and Reynolds and Luscombe[4] makes it clear that at least two systems of ranked attention exist, and that in centripetal societies where not much agonism is present (e.g. those of the gorilla and chimpanzee), display organizes the rank-ordered social relations leading to associative behaviour more like that found in the female assemblies where contact between individuals is prominent. The work of Virgo and Waterhouse on the social relations of a newly established colony of rhesus monkeys suggests that both associative and agonistic rank orders are present in rhesus societies, but since they become closely correlated, as Reynolds[5] himself found at the Whipsnade Zoo, the existence of the two has not hitherto been suspected. Both the associative rank orders of chimpanzees and the agonistic rank orders of rhesus and baboons give priority of access and are therefore comparable structures. Among chimpanzees, display gives access to preferred food, and in all other known agonistic rank orders gives priority of access to more than one type of need-satisfying object; but even here species peculiarities determine which of these or in what way the rank orders will bring this about. Bonnet macaques, though agonistically rank-ordered, do not fight over females whereas savannah baboons and rhesus do, and in his own special way the male hamadryas is sexually possessive. The Japanese workers studying the Japanese macaque select three traits in the personality of males which, by caring for one-year-old infants, are also able to be accepted into the social space occupied by the breeding hierarchy: a centre-seeking tendency, a social tendency, and aggressiveness. By identifying these characteristics we may have provided another way of describing what Reynolds and Luscombe's work now makes possible to suggest; namely, that there is both an associative and an agonistic rank order in rhesus society. If this can be shown to be so in the behaviour of other species possessing agonistically rank-ordered centripetal societies, then the great apes, the chimpanzee and the gorilla, stand out as distinct from the other centripetal societies in lacking the agonistic rank order.

The continuous cohesion of a centripetal society means that it develops a structure on the basis of a dominant individual (usually a male) surrounded by the members of the rest of the society, each of which would ideally be on a separate radius, so that threats between the members do not accidentally become directed at the dominant male. The importance of this radial axis of social orientation becomes clear in protected threat, when one individual deliberately places himself on the vector so that counter-threats towards him would be likely to precipitate counter-attacks from the dominant male. Of course, this ideal wheel-like arrangement of the members of the society is rarely uninterfered with by other influences which partly override an individual's behaviour, as when in baboon society the males place themselves between the females and a predator, but a circular radial distribution is the form towards which it tends.

A centripetal social group is therefore one in which a continuous social cohesion is maintained by the existence of a single social focus of attention around which all the social proclivities of any member of that social group are organized.

Social groupings in monkeys, apes and men

Although the members of the societies of monkeys and apes which we have been considering are not always in communication with each other – the members of bachelor bands in particular are separated often for long periods of time from immediate and continued interaction with heterosexual bands – the majority of information about these societies does concern heterosexual groups whose members remain in contact with one another and whose behaviour with respect to one another is controlled by posture, gestures and facial expressions as well as calls. Indeed, except where special circumstances bring together large numbers of the same species, as at the sleeping sites of the hamadryas baboon, the cliff feeding-groups of the gelada or the assemblies of individuals collecting at feeding sites provided by the students of the Japanese macaque, the numbers in a group rarely exceed forty or so, which is comparable to that of hunter-gatherer groups. As Lee and DeVore[6] state in their introduction to *Man the Hunter*, man has been a hunter for over 90 per cent of the two million years or so of his existence on earth. Comparison of the forms of subhuman primate social life with hunter-gatherer characteristics is therefore one of crucial importance.

Sociologists and social anthropologists recognize the 'face-to-face' group, in which all the individuals meet each other in the course of the day's activities as a primary group, in all types of human society. This kind of group is similar in kind to those which we have been considering in the subhuman primates.

Burton Benedict[7] points out that for human societies, however, 'one should distinguish between two major types of small-scale society. Both are composed chiefly of primary groups, but in one the total social field is small, and in the other it is composed of a series of interlocking similar small groups which extend through a considerable population.' In the second type the primary groups are linked together by the movement of individuals between them. Reynolds postulates that movement of individuals takes place between the primary groups of the societies of chimpanzees in an essentially similar way to what is known to occur between primary groups of human small-scale societies, e.g. the Hadza. However, the same pattern would appear to apply to the populations of most subhuman primates which maintain their primary groups not only by cohesion, but also in the case of some species by exclusion, i.e. by threatening neighbouring groups at the territory boundaries or whenever they meet within overlapping parts of their ranges.

Concerning the social differentiation within the primary group, Burton Benedict says, 'in a small-scale human society, where the total social field is small, relationships tend towards the personal pole. It matters very much more who a man is than what he does. Strong positive and negative attitudes in the role relationships in the business and professional and governmental complexes are based not mainly on role performances as shop assistants, doctors and clerks, but on family and friendship connections.' The primary groups with these characteristics in small-scale societies are what the sociologists call a community within a modern society, whereas the professional, governmental and business complex of a modern society takes the form of a formal, culturally prescribed association between the major sections of an organization and to a large extent attempt to determine the behaviour of individuals within it. Hence, modern societies contain structures or prescriptive formal associations which are brought into existence in order to organize people around the objective requirements of various economic or productive processes or even social activities, e.g. an army. In production itself, the requirements of social relationships are regarded as laid down by the requirements of the processes, and often these can be seen to cut across and interfere with the formation of communities or primary groups. These primary groups (linked into communities) tend to form wherever continuing social relations come into existence, and many of the characteristics they display will draw on deep-seated faculties within the individual which have their origin in the subhuman primate groupings of our ancestors.

Hence, it is not unreasonable to suggest that, for example, the centripetal form of attention so typical of the rank-ordered males of subhuman primates might provide an innate component which would play a decisive, creative as well as formative, role in establishing the forms of association which develop between men in groups in our complex society, as Lionel Tiger[8] worked out so ably. Similarly, more functionally oriented and more transient forms of association, such as quasi-groups or 'action-sets' discovered by Mayer[9] operating at the core of electioneering organization in India, where no organized political groups existed, may draw on modes of ranked attention which come naturally to the individual because of innate propensities in this direction.

As mentioned earlier, for 90 per cent of the time *homo sapiens* has existed on the earth he has lived as a hunter-gatherer. During this phase hunting came to be crucial in the way of life of our ancestors, and most certainly has left its mark on present-day man's social relations – especially, as Washburn and Hamburg[10] have pointed out, in the part aggression plays in our way of life. What is especially relevant to our inquiry is that hunting placed a selective advantage on forms of co-operation which required coherence between males during periods of excitement and danger. Laughlin[11] describes in detail how it is necessary to bring up the young to hunt by detailed teaching methods, but without cohort behaviour there would be no foundation on which to develop the complex relations necessary for successful hunting. Any comparison of the social life of present-day man with that of the subhuman primates must therefore take into account the influences which shaped man's nature during the

Pleistocene period, and our knowledge of hunter-gatherers, although, alas, gleaned from fragmentary material, is of crucial relevance.

Contemporary hunter-gatherer societies are of great diversity, and studies of them leave us in doubt as to whether they in fact represent the structure of the societies of the hunters of the past, and whether therefore they are typical of the mainstream of man's Pleistocene evolution. So we are obliged to gather what information is available from industrial societies and from the better documented accounts of agricultural communities.

We have been studying in the societies of monkeys and apes the predominant attention paid by all adult members of the group to a dominant, often centrally placed, individual – usually a male. This is the form which stands out as characteristic of a mode of social relations which we have termed centripetal, and which is found in both of the classificatory groups which stand closest in line to man's ancestry. Are there, we may ask, occasions in which comparable social relations are seen in our own society? That is, are there occasions when men group themselves round an individual male, or make the organization of their social behaviour dependent upon their awareness of his actions?

A charismatic leader, as defined by Max Weber,[12] demands attention by appearing in the presence of or before his followers. Such a leader recognizes no statutory values or regulations, and is thus an individual who gathers round himself a following, be it as a prophet or a military leader. These individuals arise in periods of crisis and change in industrial and agricultural societies and map out an alternative way of life. But the attention accorded them is out of all proportion to their ability to provide new and progressive ways of living: too often, war and conquest are the essence of what they have to offer. Therefore in attempting to explain charismatic movements we should look for the operation of an ethologically based attention-binding mechanism. This is not to say that tradition will not influence such movements. Norman Cohn, in *The Pursuit of the Millennium*,[13] has shown how many times in the history of Europe messianic movements drawing on a tradition of prophecy from antiquity have captured the needy and discontented masses. These movements, in general terms, can be seen as mass escapes from the disturbing reality of the times to the protection of a charismatic individual. We must emphasize that individuals capture the primitive allegiance of groups of men without necessarily having displayed a policy at that stage. This can be said of Ramsay MacDonald, Hitler and John L. Lewis. By contrast, it has been elsewhere suggested[14] that institutionalized small groups within societies (like the British Cabinet in the 'thirties) may take on a basic centripetal form.

The connection with human social life has only been briefly indicated to show in which region the connection may be found, as it is not the purpose of this book to explore the problem. Nevertheless, to understand human societies, one needs to discover the lineaments of them in subhuman primate societies. This now seems possible. In particular, the distinction between 'power' and 'influence' in human society is now seen to rest on features distinguishable in other primate societies. On the one hand, the agonistic mode coerces individuals to maintain a structure that must at all times be ready to operate to serve specific functions. On the other, there exists a cognitive set of relations reinforced by patterns of information exchange which is developed to its fullest in societies based primarily on the hedonic mode of behaviour. This feature, demonstrated clearly in the societies of the great apes, is a recent discovery and will reorient the way the study of subhuman primate societies is undertaken in the future. Man possesses the social features of both modes.

Two major features of subhuman primate social behaviour stand out. The first is the importance of the spatial properties of social organization. By looking at spatial organization, one is able to see that the escape tendencies of the individual are of primary importance in determining the basic form of the group. If the escape tendencies of the individual bring him back to the group, this maintains a continual social relationship. If not, group coherence is not maintained. We know little or nothing of man's individual escape tendencies in a group context.

Secondly, group coherence is dependent on the way the individual's tendencies produce an awareness of others in the group and/or the surrounding environment. These forms of awareness are organized differently within each mode. Because of man's enlarged environmental awareness, the selective awareness of the individual provides a dimension within which future comparison of primates, including man, can be made.

CLASSIFICATION OF
THE GENERA OF LIVING PRIMATES

(Names of species dealt with in the text are printed in italic capitals.)

	Vernacular name
Prosimii	tree-shrews
Tupaiiformes	
Tupaiidae	
Tupaiinae	
Tupaia	
Anathana	
Dendrogale	
Urogale	
Ptilocercinae	
Ptilocercus	pen-tailed tree-shrew
Lemuriformes	
Lemuroidea	Madagascar lemurs
Lemuridae	
Lemurinae	'typical' lemurs
Lemur	ring-tailed lemur
Hapalemur	
Lepilemur	
Cheirogaleinae	dwarf and mouse lemurs
Cheirogaleus	
Microcebus	
Phaner	
Indriidae	
Indri	indris
Lichanotus	
Propithecus	sifaka
Daubentoniidae	
Daubentonia	aye-aye
Lorisoidea	
Lorisidae	
Lorisinae	
Loris	slender loris
Nycticebus	slow loris
Perodicticus	potto
Arctocebus	angwantibo
Galaginae	
Galago	galagos or bushbabies
Tarsiiformes	
Tarsiidae	
Tarsius	tarsier

Anthropoidea	higher primates
Catarrhini	
Cercopithecoidea	
Cercopithecidae	Old World monkeys
Cercopithecinae	cheek-pouched monkeys
Cercopithecus	guenons
Erythrocebus	
ERYTHROCEBUS PATUS	*PATAS MONKEY*
Cercocebus	mangabeys
Mandrillus	mandrill and drill
Papio	'TYPICAL' BABOONS
PAPIO CYNOCEPHALUS	*SAVANNAH BABOONS, INCLUDING CHACMA, YELLOW, OLIVE, GUINEA, 'DOGUERA' BABOONS*
supersp.	
PAPIO HAMADRYAS	*HAMADRYAS OR SACRED BABOON*
Macaca	macaques, including:
MACACA MULATTA	*RHESUS MONKEY*
M. FUSCATA	Japanese monkey
M. RADIATA	bonnet monkey
Theropithecus	
THEROPITHECUS GELADA	*GELADA BABOON*
Colobinae	leaf-eating monkeys
Colobus	guereza or colobus
Presbytis	leaf-monkeys
PRESBYTIS ENTELLUS	*HANUMAN, COMMON or ENTELLUS LANGUR*
Pygathrix	douc langur
Nasalis	proboscis monkey
Rhinopithecus	snub-nosed monkey
Simias	Pagi Island langur
Hominoidea	
Hylobatidae	gibbons
Hylobates	
HYLOBATES LAR	*LAR GIBBON*
Symphalangus	siamang
Pongidae	great apes
Pan	
PAN TROGLODYTFS	*COMMON CHIMPANZEE*
PAN GORILLA	*GORILLA*
Pongo	
Pongo Pygmaeus	orang utan
Hominidae	
HOMO SAPIENS	*MAN*

Platyrrhini	New World monkeys
Cebidae	
Cebinae	
Cebus	capuchin monkeys
Saimiri	squirrel monkeys
Alouattinae	
Alouatta	howler monkeys
Aotinae	
Aotes	night monkey
Callicebus	titis
Atelinae	
Ateles	spider monkeys
Branchyteles	woolly spider monkeys
Lagothrix	woolly monkey
Pitheciinae	
Pithecia	sakis
Chiropotes	sakis
Cacajao	uakaris
Callithrichidae	marmosets and tamarins
Callithrichinae	
Callithrix	
Cebuella	
Leontideus	
Sanguinus	
Tamarinus	
Callimiconinae	
Callimico	

Reference Notes and Suggestions
for Further Reading

CHAPTER 2

1 Linnaeus (1758), *Systema naturae*. 10th edition.
2 Darwin, C. (1859), *The origin of species* (John Murray, London; D. Appleton, New York, 1860).
3 Simpson, G. G. (1945), 'The principles of classification and a classification of mammals'. *Bull. Am. Mus. Nat. Hist.* **85,** pp. 1–350.
4 Mivart, St G. J. (1873), 'On *Lepilemur* and *Cheirogaleus* and the zoological rank of the Lemuroidea'. *Proc. Zool. Soc. Lond.* pp. 484–510.
5 Le Gros Clark, W. E. (1962), *The antecedents of man*. 2nd edition (Edinburgh University Press; Harper & Row, New York, 1963).

Further reading

Eimerl, S. and DeVore, I. (1965), *The primates* (Time-Life, New York).
Le Gros Clark, W. E. (1965), *History of the primates*. 9th edition (British Museum [Nat. Hist.], London; University of Chicago Press, 1966).
Napier, J. R. and Napier, P. H. (1967), *A handbook of living primates* (Academic Press, New York & London).
Napier, John (1970), *The roots of mankind* (Smithsonian Institute Press, Washington).

CHAPTER 3

1 Carpenter, C. R. (1942), 'Sexual behavior of free ranging rhesus monkeys (Macaca mulatta)'. 1 and 2. *J. Comp. Psychol.* **33**, pp. 113 and 143.
2 Chance, M. R. A. (1956), 'Social structure of a colony of *Macaca mulatta*'. *Brit. J. Anim. Behav.*, vol. 4, no. 1.
3 Southwick, C. H., Beg, M. A. and Siddiqi, M. R. (1965), 'Rhesus monkeys in North India', in *Primate behavior; field studies of monkeys and apes*, ed. I. DeVore (Holt, Rinehart & Winston, New York & London).
4 Russell, W. M. S. and Russell, C. (1968), *Violence, monkeys and man* (Macmillan, London; Knopf, New York, 1970).
5 Itani, J. (1954), *The monkeys of Takasakiyama* (Kobunsha, Tokyo).

6 Southwick, C. H., Beg, M. A. and Siddiqi, M. R., ibid.

7 Reynolds, V. (1961), Ph.D. thesis, London University.

8 Simonds, P. E. (1965), 'The bonnet macaque in South India', in *Primate behavior*, ed. I. DeVore (Holt, Rinehart & Winston, New York & London).

9 Hall, K. R. L. and DeVore, I. (1965), 'Baboon social behavior', in *Primate behavior*, ed. I. DeVore (Holt, Rinehart & Winston, New York & London).

10 DeVore, I. and Washburn, S. L. (1963), 'Baboon ecology and human evolution', in *African ecology and human evolution*, ed. F. C. Howell and F. Boulière (New York Viking Fund Publication, no. 36).

11 DeVore, I. and Washburn, S. L., ibid.

12 Kummer, H. (1968), *Social organization of hamadryas baboons – a field study*. Bibliotheca Primatologica, no. 6 (S. Karger, Basel & New York).

13 Crook, J. H. (1966), 'Gelada baboon herd structure and movement – a comparative report'. *Symp. Zool. Soc. Lond.*, no. 18, pp. 237–58.

14 Kummer, H., ibid.

15 Kummer, H. and Kurt, F. (1963), 'Social units of a free-living population of hamadryas baboons'. *Folia Primatol.* **1**, pp. 4–19.

16 Jay, P. (1965), 'The common langur of North India', in *Primate behavior*, ed. I. DeVore (Holt, Rinehart & Winston, New York & London).

17 Chance, M. R. A., ibid.

18 Itani, J., ibid.

19 Sugiyama, Y. (1960), 'On the division of a natural troop of Japanese monkeys at Takasakiyama'. *Primates*, vol. 2, no. 2.

20 Sugiyama, Y. (1965), 'Behavioral development and social structure in two troops of Hanuman langurs'. *Primates*, vol. 6, no. 2, pp. 213–47.

21 Jay, P., ibid.

22 Hall, K. R. L. (1965), 'Behaviour and ecology of the wild Patas monkeys (Erythrocebus patas) in Uganda'. *J. Zool. Soc. Lond.* **148**, p. 15.

23 Carpenter, C. R. (1940), 'A field study in Siam of the behavior and social relations of the gibbon (*Hylobates lar*)'. *Comp. Psychol. Monogr.* **16**, p. 15.

24 Ellefson, J. (1966), personal communication.

25 Schaller, G. B. (1963), *The mountain gorilla; ecology and behavior* (University of Chicago Press).

26 Reynolds, V. and Reynolds, F. (1965), 'Chimpanzees of the Budongo forest', in *Primate behavior*, ed. I. DeVore (Holt, Rinehart & Winston, New York & London).

27. Goodall, J. (1965), 'Chimpanzees of the Gombe stream reserve', in *Primate behavior*, ed. I. DeVore (Holt, Rinehart & Winston, New York & London).

28 Kortlandt, A. and Kooij, M. (1963), 'Protohominid behaviour in primates'. *Symp. Zool. Soc. Lond.*, no. 10 (*The Primates*), pp. 61–88.
29 Itani, J. and Suzuki, A. (1967), 'The social unit of chimpanzees'. *Primates* vol. 8, no. 3–4, pp. 355–81.

Further reading

The accounts of the social organization of different species, together with various items of behaviour considered important by the different investigators, will be found in the book frequently referred to: *Primate behavior: field studies of monkeys and apes*, ed. I. DeVore (Holt, Rinehart & Winston, New York & London, 1965). There are also informative articles on various general topics of primate social behaviour.

Primates; studies in adaptation and variability, ed. P. Jay (Holt, Rinehart & Winston, New York & London, 1968), expands the treatment of some species by including studies of a number of different populations of the same species, and also includes certain general features.

The mountain gorilla; ecology and behavior, by George Schaller (University of Chicago Press, 1963), is a copiously illustrated study of one of the apes, and repays further examination, as does also the study of the social organization of the baboon by Hans Kummer (Chapter 3, note 12), which is distinguished by its methodology.

Also, *The apes*, by V. Reynolds (Cassell, London, and Dutton, New York, 1967); and 'Chimpanzees of the Gombe stream reserve', by J. Goodall, in *Primate behavior*, ed. I. DeVore (Holt, Rinehart & Winston, New York & London, 1965).

CHAPTER 4

1 Harlow, H. F. and Harlow, M. K. (1965), 'Affectional systems', in *Behavior of non-human primates*, vol. 2 (Academic Press, New York & London).
2 Jay, P. (1965), 'The common langur of North India', in *Primate behavior*, ed. I. DeVore (Holt, Rinehart & Winston, New York & London).
3 Sugiyama, Y. (1965), 'Behavioral development and social structure in two troops of Hanuman langurs'. *Primates*, vol. 6, no. 2, pp. 213–47.
4 Hall, K. R. L. and DeVore, I. (1965), 'Baboon social behavior', in *Primate behavior*, ed. I. DeVore (Holt, Rinehart & Winston, New York & London).
5 Hinde, R. A. and Spencer-Booth, Y. (1967), 'The behavior of socially living rhesus monkeys in their first two and a half years'. *Anim. behav.*, vol. 15, part 1, Jan., p. 169.
6 Southwick, C. H., Beg, M. A. and Siddiqi, M. R. (1965), 'Rhesus

monkeys in North India', in *Primate behavior*, ed. I. DeVore (Holt, Rinehart & Winston, New York & London).

7 Harlow, H. F. and Harlow, M. K., ibid.

9 Imanishi, K. (1957), 'Social behavior in Japanese monkeys'. *Psychologia* **1,** pp. 47–54.

10 Hall, K. R. L. and DeVore, I., ibid.

11 Kaufman, I. C. and Rosenblum, L. A. (1967), 'Depression in infant monkeys separated from their mothers'. *Science* **155,** pp. 1030–31.

12 Angst, W., personal communication.

13. Itani, J. (1959), 'Paternal care in the wild Japanese monkey (*Macaca fuscata fuscata*)'. *Primates*, vol. 2, no. 1, pp. 61–76.

14 Kaufman, I. C. and Rosenblum, L. A., ibid.

15 Kummer, H. (1968), *Social organization of hamadryas baboons – a field study*. Bibliotheca Primatologica, no. 6 (S. Karger, Basel & New York).

16 Van Lawick-Goodall (1967), 'Mother-offspring relationships in free ranging chimpanzees', in *Primate ethology*, ed. D. Morris (Weidenfeld & Nicolson, London, and Aldine Publishing Co., Chicago).

17 Segaar, J. and Nieuwenhuys, R. (1963), 'New etho-physiological experiments with male *Gasterosteus aculaetus*, with anatomical comment'. *Anim. behav.*, vol. 11, nos. 2 and 3, pp. 331–45.

Further reading

Kummer's book entitled *Social organization of hamadryas baboons – a field study*: Bibliotheca Primatologica, no. 6 (S. Karger, Basel & New York, 1968) should be consulted for the most systematic account of the development of the young hamadryas, and represents one of the most complete studies on a single species.

Schaller's *The mountain gorilla; ecology and behavior* (University of Chicago Press, 1963), contains a lot of information about the young gorilla, and amplifies considerably what has been said in this chapter.

Rheingold's *Maternal behavior in mammals* (John Wiley & Sons, New York & London, 1963) provides good background material for other mammals and also includes additional studies on one or two species of primate.

CHAPTER 5

1 Martin, R. D. (1968), 'Towards a new definition of primates'. *Man*, vol. 3, no. 3.

2 Wynne-Edwards, V. C. (1962), *Animal dispersion in relation to social behaviour* (Oliver and Boyd, Edinburgh & London, and Clarke, Irwin, Toronto).

3 Christian, J. J. (1961), 'Phenomena associated with population density'. *Proc. Nat. Acad. Sci.* **47,** pp. 428–49.

4 Chitty, D. (1952), 'Mortality among voles (*Microtus agrestis*) at Lake Vrynwy, Montgomeryshire in 1936–39'. *Phil. Trans. R.(Soc.)*, Series B, **263**, pp. 505–52.
5 Collias, N. and Southwick, C. (1952), 'A field study of population density and social organization in Howler monkeys'. *Proc. Amer. Phil. Soc.* **96**, pp. 143–57.
6 Bruce, H. M. and Parrott, D. M. V. (1960), 'Role of olfactory sense in pregnancy block by strange males'. *Science*, **131**, pp. 1526–31.
7 Murton, R. K., Isaacson, A. J. and Westwood, N. J. (1966), 'The relationships between wood pigeons and their clover food supply and the mechanism of population control'. *J. Appl. Ecol.* **3**, pp. 55–96.
8 Itani, J. (1959), 'Paternal care in the wild Japanese monkey (*Macaca fuscata fuscata*)'. *Primates*, vol. 2, no. 1, pp. 61–92.
9 Chance, M. R. A. and Russell, W. M. S. (1959), 'Protean displays; a form of allaesthetic behaviour'. *Proc. Zool. Soc. Lond.* **132**, pp. 65–70.
10 Humphries, D. A. and Driver, P. M. D. (1970–71), *Protean behaviour*. In press (Plenum Press, New York).

Further reading

Eibl-Eibesfeldt, I. (1958), 'The behaviour of rodents'. *Handbuch der Zoologie* **10** (13), pp. 1–88. (Walter de Gruyter, Berlin).
Eisenberg, J. F. (1966), 'The social organisation of mammals'. *Handbuch der Zoologie* **10** (7), pp. 1–92 (Walter de Gruyter, Berlin).

CHAPTER 6

1 Eisenberg, J. F. (1966), 'The social organisation of mammals'. *Handbuch der Zoologie* **10** (7), pp. 1–92 (Walter de Gruyter, Berlin).
2 Carpenter, C. R. (1942), 'Societies of monkeys and apes'. *Biol. Symp.* **8**, pp. 177–204.
3 Simonds, P. E., personal communication.
4 Angst, W., personal communication.
5 Crook, J. H. (1966), 'Gelada baboon herd structure and movement – a comparative report'. *Symp. Zool. Soc. Lond.* **18**, pp. 237–58.
6 Reynolds, V. and Reynolds F. (1965), 'Chimpanzees of the Budongo Forest', in *Primate behavior*, ed. I. DeVore (Holt, Rinehart & Winston, New York & London).
7 Kummer, H. (1968), *Social organization of hamadryas baboons – a field study*. Bibliotheca Primatologica, no. 6 (S. Karger, Basel & New York).
8 Rowell, T. E. (1966), 'Forest living baboons in Uganda'. *J. Zool.* **149** (3), pp. 344–65.
9 Weiss, P. (1958), 'Concepts of biology'. *Behav. Sci.* **3**, p. 93.
10 Chance, M. R. A. and Mackintosh, J. H. (1969), 'Social behaviour of the laboratory mouse'. In preparation.

11 Grant, E. C. (1963), 'An analysis of the behaviour of the male laboratory rat'. *Behav.* **21**, pp. 260–81.
12 Seward, J. P. (1945), 'Aggressive behaviour in the rat'. *J. Comp. Psychol.* **38**, pp. 175–238.
13 Kummer, H. (1957), 'Sociales verhalten einer Mantelpaviangruppe'. *Beih. Schweiz Z. Psychol.* **33**, pp. 1–91.
14 Kummer, H. and Kurt, F. (1963), 'Social units of a free-living population of hamadryas baboons'. *Folia Primatol.* **1**, pp. 4–19.
15 Schaller, G. (1963), *The mountain gorilla; ecology and behavior* (University of Chicago Press).
16 Virgo, H. B. and Waterhouse, M. J. (1969), 'The emergence of attention structure amongst rhesus macaques'. *Man*, vol. 4, no. 1.
17 Reynolds, V. and Luscombe, G. (1969), 'Chimpanzee rank order and the function of displays'. The Second Conference of the International Primatological Society, *Behaviour*, vol. I, ed. C. R. Carpenter (S. Karger, Basel & New York).
18 Jay, P. (1965), 'The common langur of North India', in *Primate behavior*, ed. I. DeVore (Holt, Rinehart & Winston, New York & London).
19 Kummer, H., personal communication.
20 Wickler, W. (1967), 'Social-sexual signals', in *Primate ethology*, ed. D. Morris (Weidenfeld & Nicolson, London, and Aldine Publishing Co., Chicago).
21 Zuckerman, S. (1932), *Social life of monkeys and apes* (Kegan-Paul, London).
22 Herbert, J. (1968), 'Sexual preference in the rhesus monkey *Macaca mulatta* in the laboratory'. *Anim. behav.*, vol. 16, part 1, pp. 120–28.
23 Herbert, J. (1970), 'Neural and hormonal factors concerned in sexual attraction between rhesus monkeys'. *Int. Prim. Cong.* II/7.

Further reading

Mayer, A. C. (1966), 'The significance of quasi groups in the study of complex societies', in *Social anthropology of complex societies*, ed. M. Banton (Tavistock Publications, London).
Morris, D. (1970), *Patterns of reproductive behaviour* (Jonathan Cape, London).
Tinbergen, N. (1959), 'Comparative studies of the behaviour of gulls (*Lariedae*) – a progress report'. *Behav.* **15**, pp. 1–70.
Mayer describes the formation of small new social groups in more complex human societies which appear to receive some explanation in terms of the structure of attention.
Tinbergen has discussed the phylogenetic implications of similarities in the repertoire of related species and the problem of distinguishing between convergent evolution and divergent evolution.

CHAPTER 7

1 Harlow, H. F. and Harlow, M. K., 'Affectional systems', in *Behavior of non-human primates*, vol. 2 (Academic Press, New York & London).

2 McCulloch, T. L. (1939), 'The role of clasping activity in adaptive behaviour of the infant chimpanzee. III. Mechanism of re-inforcement'. *J. Comp. Psychol.* **7**, pp. 305–16.

3 Mason, W. A. (1965), 'Determinants of social behaviour in young chimpanzees', chap. 9 in *Behaviour of non-human primates*, vol. 2 (Academic Press, New York & London).

4 Menzel, E., personal communication.

5 Andrew, R. (1962), 'Situations that evoke vocalization in primates', *Annals of New York Acad. Sci.* **102,** Arb. 2, pp. 296–315.

6 Berlyne, D. E. (1960), *Conflict, arousal and curiosity* (McGraw-Hill, New York & London).

7 Mason, W. A. (1964), in *Advances in experimental social psychology*, vol. 1, ed. Leonard Berkowitz (Academic Press, New York & London).

8 Kortlandt, A. and Kooij, M. (1963), 'Protohominid behaviour in primates'. *Symp. Zool. Soc. Lond.*, no. 10 (*The primates*), pp. 61–88.

Further reading

Tomkins, Silvan S. (1962–3), *Affect, imagery, consciousness*, vol. 1, *Positive affect*; vol. 2, *Negative affect* (Tavistock Publications, London; Springer New York).

Wilder, J. (1967), *Stimulus and response; law of initial value* (John Wright & Son, Bristol; Williams & Wilkins, Baltimore, 1968).

Those who are interested in the psycho-physiological mechanisms underlying the statement that 'Moderate levels of unfamiliarity therefore stimulate play, whereas higher levels of familiarity depress it and replace it by clinging,' should read the book by Wilder.

CHAPTER 8

1 Kummer, H. (1969), personal communication.

2 Angst, W. (1969), personal communication.

3 Virgo, H. B. and Waterhouse, M. J. (1969), 'The emergence of attention structure amongst rhesus macaques'. *Man*, vol. 4, no. 1, March.

4 Reynolds, V. and Luscombe, G. (1969), 'Chimpanzee rank order and the function of displays'. The Second Conference of the International Primatological Society, *Behavior*, vol. 1, ed. C. R. Carpenter (S. Karger, Basel & New York).

5 Reynolds, V. (1961), Ph.D. thesis, London University.

6 Lee, R. B. and DeVore, I., ed. (1968), *Man the hunter* (Aldine Publishing Co., Chicago).

7 Benedict, B. (1966), 'Sociological characteristics of small territories and their implications for economic development'. *The social anthropology of complex societies*, ed. Michael Banton (Tavistock Publications, London).

8 Tiger, L. (1969), *Men in groups* (Thomas Nelson, London, and Random House, New York).

9 Mayer, A. C. (1966), 'The significance of quasi-groups in the study of complex societies'. *The social anthropology of complex societies*, ed. Michael Banton (Tavistock Publications, London).

10 Washburn, S. L. and Hamburg, D. A. (1968), 'Aggressive behavior in old world monkeys and apes', in *Primates; studies in adaptation and variability*, ed. P. Jay (Holt, Rinehart & Winston, New York & London).

11 Laughlin, W. S. (1968), 'Hunting: an integrating biobehavior system and its evolutionary importance', in *Man the hunter*, ed. R. B. Lee & I. DeVore (Aldine Publishing Co., Chicago).

12 Weber, M. (1968), *Max Weber on charisma and institution building*, ed. S. N. Eisenstadt (University of Chicago Press).

13 Cohn, N. (1961), *The pursuit of the millennium* (Harper & Row, New York; Secker & Warburg, London, 1962).

14 Chance, M. R. A. (1969), 'Towards the biological definition of ethics', in *Biology and ethics*, ed. F. J. Ebling (Academic Press, London & New York).

Index

ACENTRIC SOCIETIES, 18, 180, 183, 189, 201
Acts and postures, 89, 94, 95, 102, 110, 116, 118, 119, 134, 135, 163, 164, 165, 166, 167, 168, 169, 176, 177, 182, 185, 186, 193, 194
Adoption, 124, 125, 126, 132
Aggression, 53, 57, 58, 59, 63, 69, 72, 73, 74, 166, 188, 197, 198, 207
Agonistic behaviour, 19, 53, 56, 70, 72, 73, 74, 75, 87, 89, 94, 109, 110, 142, 176, 177, 183, 199, 200, 209
Altmann, S. A., 64
Ambivalence, 122
Andrew, R., 194, 195, 196
Angst, W., 125, 158, 203
Anthropology, 14, 17
Arousal, 89, 192, 193, 194, 195, 196, 197, 198
Artificial separation, 127
Attention, 82, 87, 88, 103, 104, 105, 171, 173, 174, 175, 182, 183, 184, 198
Awareness, 133, 134, 136, 137, 201

BABOONS:
  chacma, 37, 38, 40, 66
  gelada, 37, 38, 40, 77–80, 158, 160, 186, 187, 188, 202, 205
  hamadryas, 37, 38, 39, 40, 80–85, 130, 131, 132, 161, 168, 171, 174, 178, 184, 186, 187, 188, 205
  olive, 37, 38, 40, 66
  savannah, 35, 37, 38, 39, 40, 66–77, 120–22, 123, 129, 158, 160, 162, 169, 170, 174, 175, 178, 181, 182, 185, 186, 188, 190, 191, 193, 196, 198, 200, 202, 204
  yellow, 37, 38, 40, 66
Bachelor bands, 95, 172
Beg, M. A., 51, 52, 58, 61, 65, 116
Behaviour structure, 163, 166, 168
Benedict, B., 206
Berlyne, D. E., 196
Bison, 147
Bruce, H. M., 149

CALLS, 94, 97, 111, 119, 121, 123, 198
Carpenter, C. R., 14, 49, 50, 80, 96, 97, 157
Centripetal societies, 18, 175, 180, 183, 187, 188, 189, 191, 198, 201, 207
Chance, M. R. A., 50, 59, 88, 149, 155, 164
Charismatic, 18, 19, 208
Cheetah, 145
Chimpanzee, 45, 105–13, 135–40, 158, 159, 160, 162, 170, 174, 176, 177, 188, 190, 192, 193, 194, 197, 198, 199, 200, 202, 204
Chitty, D., 148
Christian, J. J., 148, 149
Clark, Le Gros, W. E., 23
Clinging, 114, 140, 143, 198, 199
Coherence, 72, 103, 142, 143, 145, 171, 174, 191, 204, 206, 209
Cohn, N., 208
Cohorts, 63, 72, 78, 99, 109, 159, 160, 171, 202, 203, 207
Collias, N., 149
Colobus, 41, 42
Competition, 110
Core Areas, 86, 87
Crabs, 149
Crook, J., 77, 78, 160
Cycle of activity, 93, 101

INDEX

MACAQUE:
bonnet, 35, 36, 60–66, 159, 174, 185, 188, 202, 204
Japanese, 35, 53–60, 65–6, 89, 123, 126, 140, 153, 158, 159, 160, 161, 174, 188, 202, 203, 204, 205
pigtail, 124 , 127
rhesus, 35, 36, 50–53, 65, 88, 115, 116, 122, 149, 157, 159, 160, 169, 170, 175, 176, 186, 187, 188, 190, 193, 196, 198, 200, 202, 204
McCulloch, T. L., 192
MacDonald, R., 209
Mackintosh, J. H., 164
Male care of infants, 126
Malinowski, B. 17
Mammals other than primates, 144, 145, 147, 154, 169, 171
Mandrill, 35, 37, 40
Martin, R. D., 143
Mason, W., 192, 193, 194, 195, 197
Mating, 75, 166
Mayer, A. C., 207
Menzel, E., 193
Method, 13, 14, 15, 16, 36, 48, 49, 50, 51, 52, 61, 66, 67, 78, 80, 81, 86, 89, 91, 96, 97, 98, 105, 106, 192, 193, 194, 195
Mivart, St G. J., 22
Mother/infant relationships, 82, 137, 138, 139, 191, 192
Mounting, 77
Mouse, 171
Movement of groups, 53, 54, 55, 61, 68, 71, 78, 79, 81, 84, 106
Murton, R. K., 150

NIEUWENHUYS, R., 137
Non-agonistic behaviour, 134, 135, 136, 137, 138, 142
Nursing, 115, 116, 117, 123, 124, 130, 133, 192, 193, 195

ORANG-UTAN, 46, 140

PATAS MONKEY, 91–6, 158, 159, 172, 178, 182, 183, 184, 185, 186, 187, 188, 202
Peromyscus, 153, 156

Pigeons, 150
Play, 64, 94, 118, 130, 135, 138, 176, 195, 200
Polydiadic relations, 177
Population characteristics, 130, 148, 149
Predators, 110, 155, 182, 188, 192
Protean behaviour, 155, 156
Protected threat, 73, 199

RADCLIFFE-BROWN, A. R., 17
Range, 61, 101, 102, 146
Rank order, 19, 56, 57, 58, 62, 63, 65, 66, 72, 74, 102, 104, 105, 109, 117, 121, 123, 126, 140, 150, 159, 164, 168, 177, 202, 203, 204, 207
Rat, 144, 169
Red skin patterns, 187
Reflected escape, 131, 168, 169, 196, 197, 198
Relations between groups, 100, 101
Reynolds, F., 105, 106, 108, 109, 110, 160
Reynolds, V., 49, 61, 65, 103, 106, 108, 109, 110, 160, 176, 189, 200, 204, 206
Rodents, 144, 154
Role, 18, 174
Rosenblum, L. A., 124
Rowell, T. E., 162
Russell, C., 54, 58
Russell, W. M. S., 54, 58, 155

SCENT, 26, 28
Schaller, G., 14, 98, 100, 102, 103, 104, 105, 139, 175
Segaar, J., 137
Sex dimorphism, 38, 42
Sex ratio, 79, 86, 99, 100
Sexual behaviour, 59, 60, 64, 75, 83, 90, 91, 95, 102, 119, 129, 142, 186, 187
Sheep, 144, 147
Siddiqui, M. R., 51, 52, 58, 61, 65, 116
Signals, 143
Simonds, P. E., 49, 60, 61, 62, 64, 158
Simpson, G. G., 22
Sleeping habits, 70, 79, 84, 85, 86, 92, 101
Social interaction, 162, 164

INDEX